SCALING THE HEIGHTS

Measuring Scotland's Mountains

The **Munro Society**

Design and typeset by Jeremy Fenton.

Printed and bound in Great Britain by Bell & Bain Ltd., Glasgow.

Grant funding from the Scottish Mountaineering Trust.

Front cover –   *Surveying on Beinn Dearg Mòr (©Myrddyn Phillips)*

Back cover –   *Leica Viva GS15 GNSS receiver (Iain A Robertson),*
and Munro's Pocket Aneroid (JH Steward}

Contents

Foreword

Hugh Munro produced his Tables of Scottish mountains exceeding 3,000ft in height in 1891 when maps were based on the traditional surveying techniques available at the time, and in some cases were perhaps somewhat rudimentary. He and some of his colleagues in the recently formed Scottish Mountaineering Club made extensive use of aneroid barometers to check heights. He died in 1919 but the first update to the Tables, produced in 1921, incorporated many of his planned changes. This set the precedent for changing the Tables as more accurate information emerged. However, the stipulation that a top had to be at least 3,000ft high to be in the Tables was always adhered to.

The first two chapters of this book cover the creation of the Tables and the changes that have taken place over the years. However, there was always uncertainty about the status of mountains very close to the 3,000ft (914.4m) boundary. The Munro Society (TMS) was formed in 2002. In 2005/6, the media again raised the long-standing question of whether the two highest Corbetts might be Munros. TMS decided to take action to answer the question once and for all. Iain Robertson, President from 2006 to 2008, was tasked with leading this project and he describes how this expanded from checking the heights of these two Corbetts to a much more ambitious project which eventually stretched over eight years. The science behind using satellites to determine the heights of hills and mountains, together with the rigorous procedures demanded by the Ordnance Survey (OS) before it accepts revised heights, are described. The two Munros which were subsequently reclassified as Corbetts as a result of this Heighting exercise, and the one Top, which was removed from the Tables, had only been mapped as being over 3,000ft after 1973, by which time, the OS was using photogrammetry. The Munro Society Heightings project did not find any new Munros (which relieved me because I have several compleated rounds of them and was not sure how I would handle a new one!). The book includes contributions from people who took part in the Heightings programme, and it finishes with a chapter on the many hill lists which have followed on from Munro's original one. I must personally acknowledge the work put in by the editorial team in bringing this book to fruition.

This book is a fitting tribute to Hugh Munro, the centenary of whose death occurs in 2019.

Stewart Logan, President of The Munro Society, 2016 – 2018

Acknowledgements

Many people contributed to the project and the creation of this book, and The Munro Society thanks them all. In particular, we must thank the original surveyors, Jim Melville, Evangelos Pentzas and Liam Hill of CMCR Ltd., together with Graham Jackson, John Barnard and Myrddyn Phillips, who took over for the next six years. They could not have done their work without the planning by Iain Robertson and the late Alistair Milner. A big thank you must go to Alan Haworth and the late Clem Clements who kept the project going with generous donations. Additionally, we thank Susan Sharpe for undertaking the not inconsiderable task of proof reading the manuscript and Jeremy Fenton for taking the assembled manuscript for the book and preparing it for printing. The Munro Society would also like to thank the SMC's Rab Anderson and Tom Prentice for their advice regarding publication, and for putting us in touch with the Scottish Mountaineering Trust. We are extremely grateful to the Trust for providing the finance to allow this book to be printed. Lastly we must thank the very many people listed at the end of the book who acted as porters, climbers, drivers, cooks etc. The project would never have got off the ground without their help, in weather which was rarely good, normally dreich and sometimes appalling.

Editorial Team –
David Batty, Eleanore Hunter, Stewart Logan, Iain Robertson, Derek Sime, Bill Wheeler

Chapter 1

Hugh Munro's Construction of his Tables

Robin N. Campbell

Munro's Learning Curve

Hugh Munro drew up his Tables at the Scottish Mountaineering Club's (SMC) request between December 1890 (one year after the Club was formally constituted) and the summer of 1891, with publication in September 1891. There is no mention of this commission in Club papers, but there is other evidence (see below) to substantiate it. He was 34 years old when he began the task. No doubt the vigour of youth and boundless enthusiasm were essential tools for the job. His other tools were the OS one-inch and six-inch sheets,[1] together with certain other commercial maps, such as Charles Pilkington's privately-published map of the Cuillin, and the coastal Admiralty charts, supplemented by advice from other climbers — notably Norman Collie, Matthew Forster Heddle and Colin Phillip, whose knowledge greatly exceeded his own – and by his own rapidly burgeoning experience and knowledge.

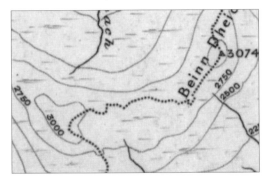 

Figure 1 – One-Inch (1886, left) and Six-Inch (1864, right) mappings of Meall Glas and Beinn Dheiceach (now Cheathaich). Beinn Dheiceach was anomalously counted as a Mountain and Meall Glas as a Top by Munro.

By the end of 1889 Munro had visited only 27 tops (counted from his Application Form and early articles in Volume I of the *SMC Journal*). In the course of the year and a half before publication he was, however, extremely active on the hills. Table 1 shows the list of his known ascents of 3,000ft hills before summer 1891, amounting to 104, to which we can add several other tops which he didn't record in the *Journal*. For example, he noted that between 7th and 9th February 1890 he climbed the four highest Cairngorm summits, but it is not at all likely that he visited just these 4 tops in the course of these excursions. He seems to have begun to press the accelerator in December 1890. Between 9th December 1890 and 29th March 1891, Table 1 shows him out and about on 18 occasions, plus 3 more days on Rum in February which were excluded from Table 1 since the tops are below 3,000ft. Table 1 shows that he was often joined during this period of activity by the Journal Editor, Joseph Stott. So Munro, and perhaps also Stott, was fast catching up with his rivals. Who were they?

---

1 Examples of these sheets are shown in Figure 1.

Munro's Rivals in the Pursuit of the Tops

Collie was never any sort of bagger, but Heddle and Phillip certainly were, as was the Reverend William Wynne Peyton. The recent biography of Heddle by Hamish H. Johnston quotes from a letter from Heddle to Archibald Geikie (April, 1890) in which he remarks that 'I have now done 350 of the 409 3000-ers, Peyton 270 – Phillip 260, others nowhere'.[2] The list of '409 3,000-ers' drawn up by Heddle has not been found. However, this information discovered by Johnston certainly transforms the context of *Munro's Tables*. Munro was not operating without example and precedent. There was an existing list of 409 3,000ft hills to guide him. We know from Johnston that Heddle carried a pocket aneroid, and measured the height of every hill he climbed,[3] and that Munro and Heddle were on good terms, enjoying an acquaintance that stretched back to a chance encounter on the box seat of the mail coach from Kingussie to Fort William on 15th October 1883.[4] Heddle had been climbing '3,000-ers' for many years by this time: for instance, he is known to have made what may well have been the first ascent of Sgùrr a' Ghreadaidh in 1871. There is much more than a good chance that Heddle made his list of 409 hills and his height data available to Munro, perhaps through the intermediation of Colin Phillip – who was particularly commended by Munro in his introduction to the Tables:

> ... when this work was first commenced, I had little idea of the enormous amount of labour and research which it would entail – a labour which, even if it had not been altogether abandoned, would have been vastly increased but for the invaluable assistance given by Mr Colin Phillip, whose extraordinary topographical knowledge of Scotland has probably never been equalled.[5]

*Sgùrr a' Ghreadaidh
(David Batty)*

---

2 *Matthew Forster Heddle: Mineralogist and Mountaineer*. National Museums of Scotland, 2015. p. 185
3 *ibid*. p. 184
4 *ibid*. p. 183
5 *SMCJ* I (1891), p. 281

Height Data used in the Tables

Whether or not Munro had access to Heddle's aneroid data, he got the bulk of his height information from the government maps, many of which had been published very recently. The 3,000ft tops are spread over 30 one-inch sheets. The number of six-inch sheets to be consulted would obviously vary considerably, with a maximum of 36 per one-inch sheet. A guestimate of 600 maps consulted in total would not be far off the mark. A complete set of one-inch Sheets for the Highlands could be purchased 'mounted and on rollers' for about £18 from the Survey. Munro would certainly have purchased a set, and may well have bought much of the six-inch Series as well. The six-inch survey was mapped (very annoyingly) by county, so that along the boundary between, say, Ross-shire and Inverness-shire two sheets partially mapping the same rectangular area had to be consulted for each stretch of the boundary, and the sheets were probably sold by county as well. The two sorts of survey sheets provided quite different information. There were no contours on the six-inch, but plenty of names, and spot heights given regularly along the watershed ridges. On the other hand, there were very few names and spot heights on the one-inch, but there were contour lines, albeit only at 250-foot intervals. So Munro's effort was indeed heroic. That there was a number of anomalies and even a mistake or two in his Tables is hardly surprising. The surprising thing is that there were so few.

His recording of height information is specified in detail in his Introduction to the Tables:

> *Height.* – When not otherwise expressly stated, all the heights given are from the six-inch Ordnance Survey. Where only one height is given – as, Ben Lomond, 3,192 – the six and one inch OS maps agree. When an exact height is followed by a height in smaller figures within parentheses, the former is from the six-inch OS, while the latter is the contour height, which is all that is given on the one-inch map – *e.g.*, Beinn Ime, 3,318 (3,250): the true height as given on the six-inch map is 3,318, while on the one-inch map there is only a 3,250 contour. 'Ap.,' following after the height, signifies that it is only approximate; the authority in most cases being careful aneroid observations taken by Dr Heddle, Mr Colin Phillip, Mr Norman Collie, Mr Hinxman, or the writer. Where *only* a contour height is given – as, Meall a' Bhàrr (Càrn Mairg) – no figure is given on the six-inch and only a contour height on the one-inch.[6]

There are 50 cases in the 1891 Tables where a height is qualified by 'Ap.', and these are shown in Table 2, identified by 1997 Table names where these are available, and 1891 Table names where they are not. The hill identifiers from the Variorum Table in my *Munroist's Companion* are also given, together with the source surveyor identified by initials. It is apparent from Table 2 that most of these data were contributed by Heddle and Phillip, and that in general the agreement with modern height data is satisfactory, with an average error of 13 feet of underestimate.

The Scottish Mountaineering Club has – on loan from the Munro family – Munro's pocket aneroid, an instrument made by JH Steward of The Strand, and his pocket thermometer, made by CW Dixey of New Bond Street – spectacles-makers to the rich

---

6   *SMCJ* I (1891), p. 279

and famous.[7] These instruments are shown in Figure 2.

So while there is little doubt that Munro had a great deal of aneroid-derived height data available to him, it is also clear that his policy was only to publish such data if there were no better data – i.e. government-approved data obtained by levelling – available.

Figure 2 – Munro's pocket aneroid (JH Steward) and thermometer (CW Dixey)

The Commissioning of the Tables

As noted in my first paragraph, there is no record in official Club papers that Munro was asked to compile his Tables. However, at the very end of Table II in Volume I of the *SMC Journal*, Joseph Stott added a note:

> The immense extent of the labour undertaken by Mr Munro will be apparent even on the most cursory survey of his 'Tables'. Measured merely by time, the compilation has to my knowledge – *for I have been somewhat of a task-master in the matter* [my italics] – occupied over 300 hours during some five months. It may be affirmed without fear of contradiction that so complete, exhaustive, and instructive a list has never before been put together, and that it forms a contribution to Scottish orography whose value it would be difficult to exaggerate. There is little doubt that the lists will receive the study they deserve at the hands of all who are interested in the mountains of Scotland. – ED [Joseph G. Stott][8].

So, according to Stott's account, Munro began his task around the start of 1891. There is further information about the effort made by Munro to distinguish between mountains and tops in his obituary written by William Douglas in 1919:

> These Tables involved an immense amount of research, of much poring over six-inch maps, and of special visits to certain tops to decide doubtful points. I remember meeting him one evening at Joe Stott's when the list was in preparation, and I have a vivid recollection of his enthusiasm as we discussed what was a mountain and what was a top till the small hours of the morning. I afterwards heard of a great visit paid to Sir Colin Phillip's in

7 Dixey's website carries the boast that 'Our distinguished patrons have included Sir Winston Churchill, seven Kings and Queens of England, Napoleon Bonaparte, Emperor Qianlong of China, and James Bond creator, Ian Fleming.'
8 *SMCJ* I (1891), p. 314

Arran, where 'hills and tops' were discussed for three days and three nights with but little intermission.[9]

It is a great pity that neither of these fascinating discussions made their way into print. However, the important point here is that this is further evidence that Munro was not operating independently, but was preparing his Tables under the guidance of other prominent Club members.

What is a Mountain and what is a Top? View of Braeriach to Ben Macdui (David Batty)

The First Revision of *Munro's Tables*, 1921

Although Munro died in 1919, he was nevertheless in charge of the revision of his Tables planned to appear in a Club publication – referred to here as Young (1921) – dealing with general aspects of Scottish mountaineering.[10] Indeed, Munro took a strong proprietary interest in his Tables. For example, at the 1903 AGM of the Club, it was reported that 'Mr Alex. Fraser moved reprinting of Volumes I and II of the *Journal*. This was vetoed by Mr Munro, who claimed copyright in *Munro's Tables*'.[11]

After Munro's death, his family passed over to the Club his personal copy of the 1891 Tables, his Card Index of tops – containing changes in classification, new tops, cancelled tops, etc., and a notebook prepared for Munro by Alexander W Peacock itemizing the relevant changes in OS maps subsequent to 1891,[12] but there seems to have been nothing in the way of a new text for the revised Tables.

---

9 *SMCJ* XV (1919), p. 215. Colin Phillip has been mistakenly granted a knighthood by Douglas.
10 This was eventually published in 1921 with the catchy title *The Scottish Mountaineering Club Guide. Volume I, Section A.* (edited by James R. Young). Later versions were titled *General Guide-Book*.
11 *SMCJ* VIII (1904), p.74. Even in 1903, there was a severe shortage of these early volumes, which was the reason for Fraser's motion.
12 These three documents are in the Club Archives held by the National Library of Scotland – Acc.11538, items 116, 117 and 120 respectively. Peacock's notes relate to the two revisions of the one-inch map and one revision of the six-inch map published by the Survey since 1891, involving many changes of name and height, etc. For more information there is a helpful note by James Gall Inglis on p.115 of Young (1921). Item 116 is a bound volume. There were other bound volumes of the 1891 Tables distributed by Munro. One, dedicated in Munro's hand to A.E. Robertson, is in the Club Library.

In the Prefatory Note to the Revised Tables (Young, 1921, p. 109), President William Ling enumerated the scanty records left by Munro, described in the preceding paragraph, and acknowledged the difficulty of proceeding with a new text under these circumstances. Young published the new Tables as 'Revised by the Compiler, the late Sir Hugh T. Munro, and rearranged by Mr J Gall Inglis'. In fact, there was very little revision of the main text. As for Table I, name and height changes following the new maps were recorded, a number of new footnotes added, and an Appendix listed the promotions, demotions and eliminations signalled in the Card Index.

In 1991, I published an article about the 1891 Tables in which I observed that there were eight height anomalies in Table I of the following sort: two adjacent tops have so little drop between them that only one can be a 'separate mountain', but in the Table the *lower* of the two tops was given separate mountain status.[13] This observation showed that in 1891 Munro did not consider height to be fundamental in making the distinction between Mountains and Tops. But all of these anomalies were corrected in the Revised Tables, and in three cases Munro added the explanation 'being highest point'.

It is my view that in 1891 Munro considered various other properties in addition to height, drop and distance when deciding whether to count a top as a distinct and separate mountain. These additional properties included a) whether the top was named on both scales of map, b) whether it was decorated with a cairn, and c) whether it belonged to a named mountain range. By the time he was planning the revision, his fellow mountaineers had supplied cairns almost everywhere, and the Survey had transferred the names of tops in the 1891 Table I from the six-inch to the one-inch, so that he was obliged to give up a) and b), although he clung on to c), as did the Club until the Brown-Donaldson revisions of 1981.

The observations of this section make it plain that Munro was in favour of revision of his Tables in the light of new government data, that he was largely responsible for the substantive changes between the 1891 and 1921 Tables, and that he was also not averse to changing the criteria for determining 'distinct and separate mountain' status. And most certainly those who wish to adhere to the 'Holy Writ of Munro' should seek for it in the 1921 Tables rather than in the original Tables, and should bear in mind that there is ample evidence (gathered here) that he was always ready to give new OS-endorsed data precedence over his original data.

Finally, we come to the vexed question of the Inaccessible Pinnacle. It is one of the 1891 anomalies, since there it is marked in both Tables as a Top of the distinct and separate mountain Sgùrr Dearg. Although the roles are reversed in the 1921 Tables, there is no helpful footnote, nor any entry in the list of changes on p. 134. So did Munro sanction the change? The Index Cards are difficult to interpret, since they are annotated in various hands, up to and including Robin Gall Inglis. Did Munro discount 'being highest point' in the case of the Inaccessible? If he did, his grounds must have been orographical. Sgùrr Dearg is the culminating point of three great ridges, whereas the Inaccessible is a mere and temporary excrescence on Sgùrr Dearg's south-east ridge. Guides who earn their living by making the Inaccessible accessible should perhaps bow

---

13 *Munro's Tables 1891-1991*, SMCJ XXXV (1991), pp. 21-27. Reproduced as Chapter 4.8 in my *The Munroist's Companion* (Scottish Mountaineering Trust, 1999).

down every morning and bless the names of James Gall Inglis and James R. Young, and mountaineers who wish to adhere to the Holy Writ of Munro when traversing the Munros must visit the Fisherfields and their like, and many rather dull Cairngorm tops, but need not bother with the lower tops in the named ranges of Liathach, Beinn Eighe, etc., and they may be content to gaze upwards in admiration at the lofty Inaccessible of Skye while resting on its parent summit of Sgùrr Dearg.

Left: Sgùrr Dearg and the Inaccessible Pinnacle – the culminating point of 'the three great ridges' (David Batty)

Below: Liathach from the south (Derek Sime)

Table 1. Ascents of 3,000ft hills by Hugh Munro before publishing his Tables. Italicized hills are repeat ascents. All sources are his (retrospective) Application Form for membership, or *SMC Journal* Volume I.

Date	Hills traversed	Companions	Source
5-79	Ben Lawers	?	App. Form
6-85	Stob Coire Gaibhre, Stob a' Choire Leith, Stob Coire Cath na Sgine, Caisteal, Stob Coire an Laoigh, Beinn na Socach	?	App. Form
24-4-86	Carn nan Gabhar, Braigh Coire Chruinn Bhalgain	?	App. Form
26-4-86	Schiehallion	?	App. Form
28-4-86	Ben Nevis	?	App. Form
9-86	Aonach Mor, Top of An Cul Choire, Stob Coire an Fhir Dhuibh, Tom na Moine	?	App. Form
8-87	Ben Wyvis	?	App. Form
12-2-88	Meall Odhar, Glas Maol, Cairn na Glasha, Tom Buidhe	'with a neighbour'	I, p. 23-4
1-4-88	*Cairn na Glasha*	'with a friend'	I, p. 100-1
6-4-89	Stobinian, Ben More	G.G. Ramsay + 3	I, p. 21
5-89	Sgurr na Lapaich (Affric), Mam Sodhail, Sgurr na Fhuaran, Sgurr na Carnach, Ben Sgriol	Alone	I, p. 129-30
1-1-90	Broad Cairn, Carn Bannoch, Cairn Taggart, Lochnagar	Alone	I, p. 102
3-1-90	Beinn Iutharn Mor, Glas Tulaichean	Alone	I, p. 103
6-2-90	Driesh, Mayar, *Tom Buidhe*, Tolmount, Fafernie, *Cairn Taggart*	Alone	I, p. 104
7,8,9-2-90	Carn Toul, Braeriach, Ben Macdhui and Cairngorm	Alone	I, p. 105
11-2-90	Mount Keen	Alone	I, p. 105
3-8-90	Beinn Ghlas, *Ben Lawers*, An Stuc, Meall Garbh, Meall Gruaidh	J.G Stott and another	I, p. 131-2
4-8-90	Carn Gorm, Meall Garbh, Carn Mairg, Creag Mhor	J.G. Stott and another	I, p. 132
7-9-90	Ben More, Mull	'with a friend'	I, p. 177
9-12-90	Sgairneach Mhor, Beinn Udlamain	Alone	I, p. 176
10-12-90	Geal Charn, Bruach nam Iomairean	Alone	I, p. 176
11-12-90	Carn na Caim	Alone	I, p. 176
21-12-90	Creag na Caillich, Beinn nan Eachan, Meall Garbh, Meall nan Tarmachan, Meall Ghaordie	J.G. Stott	I, p. 178
22-1-91	Carn Liath	Alone	I, p. 243
10-2-91	Sgor nan Coireachan, Sgor Choileam	Alone	I, p. 243
11-2-91	Carn Beag Dearg, Carn Dearg Mheadhonach, Carn Mor Dearg	Alone	I, p. 244
13-2-91	An Gearanach	Alone	I, p. 244
21-2-91	*Fafernie*, *Cairn Taggart*, Unnamed [152], Cairn Corbreach, Little Pap, Meikle Pap, *Lochnagar*, Meall Coire na Saobhaidhe	J.G. Stott	I, p. 242
22-2-91	Carn Aosda, Cairnwell	J.G. Stott	I, p. 242
14-3-91	Meall Corranaich, Meall a' Choire Leith	C.B. Phillip	I, p. 241
22-3-91	Carn Dearg, Unnamed [474], Lancet Edge, Geal Charn, Aonach Beag, Beinn Eibhinn, Top 3350ft, Meall Glas Choire	Alone	I, p. 245
23-3-91	Beinn Bheoil, Sron Coire na h-Iolaire	Alone	I, p. 246
24-3-91	Garbh Mheall, and its lower top	Alone	I, p. 246
26-3-91	Beinn Vannoch, Beinn a' Chuirn	Alone	I, p. 246
27-3-91	Beinn Bhuidhe	W. Douglas, Stott +2	I, p. 237
28-3-91	Beinn Eunaich	J.G. Stott	I, p. 238-9
29-3-91	Beinn Bhuiridh, Stob Daimh, Drochaid Glas, Beinn Cruachan	F. Campbell, J. Gibson, J. Rennie	I, p. 240
2-5-91	Sron Garbh, Mullach Coire nan Iubhair, Creag Peathraich, Beinn a' Chlachair	J. Rennie	I, p. 321
3-5-91	Ben Alder	Gibson, L. Hinxman, Rennie	I, p. 322
4-5-91	Beinn Dearg (Atholl), Carn Clabhainn	Gibson, Hinxman, Rennie, Stott	I, p. 323-4

Table 2. Aneroid data used in 1891 Tables. 1997 Table names are used unless the top has been deleted. Surveyors: CBP–Colin Phillip; MFH–Matthew Heddle; HTM–Hugh Munro; JNC–Norman Collie; LH–Lionel Hinxman; Cpt. K–Capt. Kirkwood, R E (from Kinlochewe Visitors Book).

1997 Name	Variorum ID	1891 Ht.	1997 Ht.	Error	Surveyor
Meall nan Aighean	LY02	3200	3218	-18	CBP
Meall Garbh	LY07	3200	3176	+24	CBP
Beinn Ghlas	LT06	3657	3619	+38	MFH
[Sron dha-Murchdi]	LT07	3040	3097	-57	HTM
Meall Corranaich	LT08	3530	3507	+23	HTM
Meall Garbh	LT11	3369	3366	+24	MFH
Beinn nan Eachan	LT12	3265	3281	-16	MFH
Sgiath Chùil	MF10	3050	3022	+28	MFH, CBP
Stob na Doire	CO02	3250	3317	-67	CBP
Stob an Fhuarain	AP01	3160	3176	-16	MFH
An Gearanach	MA08	3200	3222	-22	HTM
An Garbhanach	MA09	3200	3199	+1	HTM
[Stob Coire an Fhir Dhuibh]	NE09	3580	3504	+76	MFH
Stob Coire na Ceannain	GC10	3720	3684	+36	MFH
Stob Coire na Gaibhre	GC11	3150	3143	+7	CBP
Meall na Teanga	WL02	3050	3012	+38	MFH
Garbh Chìoch Mhòr	DK02	3365	3323	+42	MFH
Garbh Chìoch Bheag	DK03	3100	3176	-76	MFH
Sgùrr na Forcan	SA05	3100	3159	-59	CBP
Meall an Fhuarain Mhor	AT02	3150	3130	+20	CBP
Tom a' Chòinnich Beag	AF24	3450	3386	+64	MFH
Meall Dearg	TO04	3150	3133	+17	JNC
Am Fasarinen	TO05	3050	3041	+9	JNC
Stob a' Choire Liath Mòr	TO07	3200	3225	-25	JNC
Stùc a' Choire Dhuibh Bhig	TO08	3000	3002	-2	LH
Spidean Coire nan Clach	TO12	3220	3258	-38	MFH, CBP
[Slioch]	LF01	3260	3215	+45	Cpt. K
A' Mhaighdean	LF03	3100	3173	-73	MFH, CBP
Mullach Coire Mhic Fhearchair	LF04	3320	3340	-20	MFH, CBP
Sgùrr Creag an Eich	TE04	3350	3337	+13	MFH
Lord Berkeley's Seat	TE05	3300	3379	-79	CBP
Corrag Bhuidhe	TE06	3360	3435	-75	MFH
Stob Cadha Gobhlach	TE07	3040	3150	-110	MFH
Glas Mheall Liath	TE08	3080	3150	-70	MFH
Sgùrr Breac	FA02	3240	3278	-38	CBP
Cona' Mheall	GU02	3200	3209	-9	CBP
Ben More Assynt, South Top	AS02	3200	3150	+50	MFH
[Big Brae]	EC02	3100	3091	+9	CBP
Sgor an Lochain Uaine	BC05	4095	4127	-32	LH
Creag an Dubh-loch	DO09	3100	3225	-125	HTM
Carn a' Choire Bhoidheach	SD03	3630	3642	-12	HTM
Creag a' Ghlas-uillt	SD04	3450	3504	-54	HTM
Am Bàsteir	SK04	3020	3064	-44	JNC
Sgùrr a' Ghreadaidh	SK06	3100	3189	-89	JNC
Sgùrr Dearg, Inaccessible Peak	SK09	3250	3235	+15	JNC
Sgùrr Thearlaich	SK10	3210	3209	+1	JNC
Sgùrr Alasdair	SK11	3255	3255	+0	JNC
Sgùrr Dubh an Da Bheinn	SK13	3080	3077	+3	JNC
Sgurr Dubh Mòr	SK14	3110	3097	+13	JNC

Chapter 2

Always Changing, Never Changing

Hamish M. Brown

When I was asked to write something about 'the thinking behind the post-World War II amendments to *Munro's Tables*' I was somewhat stumped. The thinking post-war was no different from any which had gone before: to continue revising as and 'when more complete information was available,' something which Munro himself was about when he died. The Tables never have been static. They couldn't be. However, I can make some observations, and no doubt fail with the best to heed the admonition in the Preface to the Scottish Mountaineering Club's first Journal (1891): 'Let thy words be few'.

This Preface also noted, 'Probably it will surprise many readers to learn that there are more than three hundred mountains in Scotland where height exceeds 3,000ft above sea level'. Many 'were undescribed and some perhaps unvisited except for shepherds, foresters and sportsmen'. Popular guidebooks might mention as many as sixty but the mountain knowledge was there, though seemingly untapped by Munro and helpers. A volume like Robert Hall: *The Highland Sportsman and Tourist* (annually 1882-1885) lists every hill of every height in every estate and various multi-volume gazetteers (mine the volumes of Groome) gives remarkable topographical information. Local shepherds, foresters and sportsmen (i.e. shooters) indeed did know their ground. The varied climbers who gelled into the Scottish Mountaineering Club (SMC) in 1889 were coming at the hills in a different way and because they were few and a close-knit bunch were largely unaware of any others' doings. I'm convinced there were more hill ascents than generally believed. Even Queen Victoria published accounts of climbing hills (Munros at that), Ben Lomond had been over-run since the end of the 18th Century, and quite ordinary working class people were no less prepared to go up a hill for fun.[1]

Hugh Munro (he only became Sir Hugh in 1913), an enthusiastic original member of the SMC which was founded in 1889, started a journal (SMCJ) in 1890 and in the sixth number of volume one, 1891, the *Tables* first appeared. The club membership then was small so the *Tables* were not known about generally. Some obviously thought the *Tables* 'a good thing' for A E Robertson, in a blitz of only a few seasons, became the first to do them all in 1901.

The term 'Munro' seemed to have been used very early on. The SMCJ (May 1895) has '… peak-bagging … the mystic "Munros" altitude …' and A E Robertson in the SMCJ, 1902, reporting his 1901 compleating,[2] entitles the article '*The Munros' of Scotland*. Burn,

---

1   Some of this is covered in Ian R Mitchell: *Scotland's Mountains Before the Mountaineers* (Luath Press, 1998). In a recent *Travels in Scotland 1788-1881* (Λ J Durie) 2012 there is a chapter reproducing an 1881 diary (with drawings) showing a working class family ascent of Beinn Ime, which was not considered anything extraordinary; the same volume shows Ben Lomond as a popular objective for all and sundry, not just 'mountaineers'.

2   Compleating is the idiosyncratic traditional spelling which I'm happy to use, especially as some find it completely annoying. Munro, failing on the In Pin and dying with only two other Munros to do rather forced me to compleat in a panic in 1965. I only had two to go and was heading off for three months' winter climbing in the Atlas. What if I died or managed to kill myself out there? So I made siccar – and even won a bonus as a later revision promoted the hill I'd traversed between the two.

Munroist No 2, freely used the term.

In the SMCJ for 1893 there is a *six-page* coverage of H T Munro's *Additions, Corrections and Remarks* for his *Tables*. 'It was of course inevitable that the *Tables* should contain some inaccuracies, and I am gradually collecting information and correcting them … Other members may like to follow my example'. Plenty did so. And it was only in Donaldson's 1974 metric edition that *hundreds* of footnotes, by dozens of contributors, were at last abandoned. Almost every hill had some additional comment on it: height, name, position, contradictions on different map scales, etc., etc. The *Tables* were a bit of a mess in fact. (The maps of Munro's time only showed 250 foot contours, if any, on the higher reaches, the very place where the greater accuracy was needed by mountaineers.)

The blessing today is the *Tables'* compact yet comprehensive layout, and with useful maps. Munro would give three cheers if he could see them. And what would he make of a Society bearing his name and composed of compleaters, male and female? It took a century to reach this greater certainty. The changes came bit by bit: 'County' was dropped, then 'Best ascended from', an introduced four figure reference became a six figure reference, with the Landranger sheet number given. A two page spread became a page and a half and finally the one page. Maps and illustrations came in 1974. Munro's intentions could not have been carried out better, at any time, an exercise driven by the constant resurveying and changes by the Ordnance Survey.

The *Tables* never will be perfectly defined, lacking the exact definition of Corbetts, Grahams, etc. Improving has always had to bear with the original anomalies, which of course leaves any revisioning wide open to criticism. Do not blame the succession of editors; they were employed by the Club and what they produced had to receive the Club's approval. The *Tables* are the jealous possession of the Club, theirs the moral and legal rights. (Incidentally, to use the term 'Munros' for anything other than the list of *Scottish* 3,000-ers is both wrong and illegal, and could lead to a prosecution!)

With the steady early growth of the SMC and presumably knowledge of the *Tables* leaking to other mountainy folk there was a call to reprint volumes one and two of the SMCJ. (At the end of volume 3 there is a note from a gentleman in Manchester offering 2/6d each for volumes 1 or 2.) This reprinting was vetoed by Munro (at the 1903 AGM) as he was still working to see the *Tables* revised and obviously did not want to see the now deficient original continued. I wonder if those who have aye girned, 'the *Tables* should be as Munro made them' realise just how 'primitive' the mapping detail was at that time. (Heavens! When I started ticking with the 1953 edition there were hummings and hawings over Beinn Tarsuinn in the wilds north of Loch Maree. Everyone knew it was a Munro, but not the OS. And I recall doing a 1,000ft rock climb in that area on ground shown as 'rough pasture'.) The early years had endless apologetic notes, such as for the Cuillin, which were 'taken from Mr Pilkington's new map which is more accurate than the Ordnance Survey' and 'heights from aneroid observations by Mr. Norman Collie'. (An echo of this in the recent activities of today's dedicated surveyors whose latest technology, measuring to mere centimeters, is then accepted by the OS and, perforce, the SMC and the next *Tables* revision.) There were many problems with heights with variations on one-inch and six-inch maps and one or the other not even giving a summit name. 'It is inevitable that there should be some mistakes … what are to be considered distinct and separate mountains and what may be counted as "tops" … cannot be finally insisted on'.[3] And there lies all the justification for the continual revisions as the data have changed in a century of OS mapping and with the *Tables* trying to keep up, as Munro wanted.

In 1921 the SMC published a *General Guide* which included the *Tables* (cost 7/6, postage 3d). Topics covered were Geology, Meteorology, Botany, Bird Life, Equipment, Maps, Rock Climbing, Snow Craft – and Hugh Munro's *Classified Tables of the 3,000ft mountains of Scotland*, which had had some tweaking, even then. Gall Inglis noted at the time 'The heights and hill-names in the six-inch map, and sometimes the position of the latter, do not always agree with those on the one-inch sheet'. This sounds almost like a *crie de coeur* that creating accurate *Tables* was an impossible task, a feeling with which every editor since will sympathise. In 1981, when I was involved, the OS had still not been persuaded to have all Munros named on their maps.[4]

One anomaly that disappeared in 1921 was seeing the higher Inaccessible Pinnacle swop with Sgùrr Dearg as being the Munro. Maybe here we have a reason why some demand only the 'original' listing should be regarded as *Munro's Tables*: the original list would let them off climbing the In Pin! Munro of course intended to climb it as he was climbing everything (both Munros and Tops), an intention which too few today are emulating. Unattributed pencilled notes on Munro's card index indicate that there was a proposal for this In Pin correcting. That only two years passed between Munro's death and this publication must indicate a general agreement as to what he had intended. The SMC was a small coterie and the Tables were very much theirs. Of the first 32 compleaters (1957) half were SMC members with A E Robertson (1901) the only pre-1921 compleater. There were only 8 completions before World War Two.

Eric Maxwell, Munros, Tops and Deletions 1957, Furths 1958, is No. 30 on the list. (In 1966 he had repeated all this, except the Furths.) He was a keen member of the Grampian Club and, after his compleations, produced a leaflet entitled *Quad Erat Faciendum* which listed all the Munroists and their details up to that time. He notes:

> Whilst one can sympathise with those who object to alteration of what is a historic document, there must clearly come a time when all references to earlier data are omitted, and only the most recent information used.

The 1921 General Guide was reissued in 1929 and then in 1933 there was a new, revised, edition with the Equipment chapter updated and 'Photography' by Percy Donald

---

3   As stated by Hugh Munro in his Introduction to the original Tables.
4   In 1981 Bartholomew's, the mapmakers, asked me to mark Munros on their half-inch maps and this I did at the campsite in Essaouira during a break from Atlas explorations. I'd my campervan on the site and could spread maps everywhere and worked away at the task – to the great curiosity of another GB camper nearby where the couple eventually just had to ask what I was doing. (They became good friends over the following decades.) Sadly, Bartholomew's sold out and their attractive maps were no longer published, so my work was never used.

As an aside on this aside, the great Polish Map of Scotland, the football-pitch sized 3-D map created at Eddleston (near Peebles) was painted in the contour colours of Bartholomew's maps. This 'thank you Scotland' creation by wartime Polish Forces was a walled, sunken, accurate, scale map of Scotland, set in surrounding 'sea' and with major rivers flowing. It became overgrown and lost but is now fully restored to its former extraordinary glory. Visit! It lies just across the ravine from the Barony Castle Hotel. (www.mapascotland.org).

added. You cannot have guides that do not update. For years after maps went metric I knew hillgoers who stuck with their 'good old one-inch'. Do those who clamour for 'No changes!' refuse Gore-Tex and clump about in hobnails?

Another reverend would become the second Munroist in 1923 [5], Ronald Burn, and he was also the first to record doing the Tops as well (1923) and, in Maxwell, he is noted as doing 'Deletions'. Obviously, there were rumblings over losing Tops right from the beginning so a few topped-up with these, something which soon died out (Maxwell only lists a handful) and would require a Herculean effort to re-create today with over a century of changes to names, heights and even position on maps.

Robin Campbell (who else?) has actually listed all the changes through all the editions, what he called *A Variorum Table of the Munros and Tops*. This occupies *35 pages* (the least read?) in his tremendous compendium *The Munroist's Companion* (SMT 1999).[6] That book scalpels into every possible cranny of Munroitis so my writing at all is really superfluous.

The *Tables* I first encountered, and used, was the 1953 edition of R Gall Inglis, the first volume to add the tables of Corbetts and Donalds. (The aim of walkers at that time was to climb the 276 Munros, or 277 including Tarsuinn – which only took its place in 1974.) This edition still sprawled over two pages and lacked six figure references but it was the *Tables* that really caught the public's attention. The war was over, the outdoors beckoned and here was a game, a challenge, that could be taken on by anyone. Numbers compleating increased through the Sixties, and in the Seventies took off (shorter working days, cars, etc.) and, with the OS re-surveyings, led to the first 'metric' maps (remember those weird contours?) which called for new *Tables* in 1974, edited by Jim Donaldson.

Jim was the long-time SMC Treasurer and SMC President, 1976-1978. He compleated in 1961 (No 43). The heights were still taken from the one-inch and six-inch OS maps but also given metric heights 'for the coming metrification'. The 'Best ascended from' column was dropped. Tarsuinn was now 3,070 (2,850c on the one-inch still!) There were two new Munros, two new Tops, two re-sited summits and eight Tops were deleted as below the height – noted from the 1:10,000 maps. The book was at last given useful diagrammatic maps by Jim Renny and illustrations were introduced.

This first metric edition of the *Tables* of 1974 was, in many ways, a stopgap, to have at least something available while the OS slowly delivered metric maps, on which appeared a great deal that differed, so every height, position, etc., had to be checked for 1981. I

---

5   J A Parker was Munroist No. 3 in 1927 and the first to add the Furths (1929); J Rooke Corbett was No. 4, also with the Tops (1930) and of course created the list of 2,500ft hills that bears his name, mercifully with the re-ascent definition; while William Docherty, No. 13, became the first to compleat the Munros, Tops and Furths, in 1949.

6   *The Munroist's Companion* should be in the possession of all Munroists, being a mine of all things to do with the subject. Chapter 1 is all about or by Munro, Ch 2 ditto for A E Robertson, Ch 3 covers Burn, Parker, Corbett and Dow, Ch 4 is about defining and classifying, Ch 5 is the Variorum, Ch 6 historic advice, Ch 7 predicaments and Ch 8 some modern doings. There's also good Munro material in W D Brooker's anthology *A Century of Scottish Mountaineering* (SMT) 1988, reprinted 1993. The only other extensive book on Munros is Andrew Dempster's *The Munro Phenomenon* (Mainstream) 1995.

joined Jim Donaldson as junior editor.[7] There was a pretty clear idea of what needed to be done but, as usual with these types of decision the result was a compromise and, to me and many, some glaring anomalies were still left. I did argue for a more radical revision to give the list a logical uniformity (changes which were made later of course) so was a bit peeved when much of the public criticism (too much changed, not enough changed) was levelled at me.

Just how much needed tidying up can be seen in how a 'considerable protuberance' in the middle of Perthshire was found to be out by 400ft![8] It became a new Corbett and there were something like 17 of these added, which passed largely without comment, as Corbetteers were fewer in number and a bit more grown up than Munroists. Catching up on these new Corbetts gave me many memorable hill days so I have never understood why our giving An Teallach and Liathach justifiable second Munros raised such a furor. To *grudge* a visit to An Teallach or Liathach (often voted our two best hills) was weird but the complaints also gave me an element of satisfaction: if people had given these fine hills the treatment they deserved, rather than a mere up-down for a tick, they would have gained a bonus.

'A considerable protuberance' – Sròn a' Choire Chnapanich in the foreground (David Batty)

---

7 I'd completed Munros in 1965 (No 62) but by 1981 had done five rounds, (and five Furths) including the 1979 first-ever continuous Munro 'walk'. My Corbetts had been completed in 1975 and only a handful of Donalds remained unclimbed in 1981. I knew the ground thoroughly! (I'd also been running weeks of courses in Ireland, months of trips in Morocco, climbed and skied in Spain and Corsica and made a trek, Banachdich to Keen) and was planning the 'Groats End Walk'. Somehow the *Tables*' work was fitted in.
8 Sròn a' Choire Chnapanich (NN456453 at the top of Glen Lyon).

An Teallach's two Munros – Sgùrr Fiona & Bidean a' Ghlas Thuill (David Batty)

Jim Donaldson in the SMCJ of 1981 (the year of the newest *Tables*, Donaldson/Brown version) had a delightful skit on 'Ben Feskineth – a Lost Munro?' and Keeper of the List, Bill Brooker, in 1991 had an article *Rampant Munrosis: the Scottish Disease* which, oh dear, some took so seriously. (I was lampooned as a 'Polymunroist'). The SMC has always had a not-too-serious relationship with its Munro inheritance, which no doubt also contributed to outside, pedantic, criticism. Number 276 in the list of compleaters was always reserved for 'the unknown Munroist' (276 for many years being the vital number) and 666 omitted as being the evil 'number of the beast' and all that. An aside to lighten this serious business.

On one of my *Munros* working visits to Jim I was staying at Braemar youth hostel on some ploy and had returned there after a pleasant evening with Jim and Sheila. Jim was a member of the Braemar Mountain Rescue Team. Before going to bed I took the opportunity of washing every item of clothing but was barely asleep before the warden crept in to tell me Jim had telephoned. There was a callout. Could I come? Well, actually, no. I'd no clothes to wear.

Jim's 1974 edition had been a far more useful revision than what we did in 1981, which was mostly checking all the heights and other changes resulting from the new OS maps. The title page still noted 'Revised by the compiler, the late Sir Hugh Munro of Lindertis and rearranged by J Gall Inglis'. We were only doing what others had done before us and, like them, were hampered by conservative opinions, within and outwith the SMC. Reprints with minor revisions followed in 1984 and 1990 but the Derek Bearhop edition of 1997 gave the – at last – rigorous, consistent revision that dealt with nearly all the anomalies: 9 new Munros forsooth (and +9, -15 Tops) where Jim and I had only added two (which caused the fuss). Bearhop never received the same criticism as the Donaldson/Brown edition. Perhaps change as inevitable was finally accepted, perhaps any discontent has simply been swamped by the tsunami of Munro-bagging today. The term 'Munros' can even be bandied about at Westminster without any need of explanation and duly appear in Hansard.

Ben Lui NW Top, which first appeared in the Tables in the 1984 edition and was deleted from the Tables in the 1997 edition (Derek Sime)

The SMC had been rather ambivalent about *Munro's Tables*, with some members wishing that they had never happened ('nothing to do with mountaineering!'). Others (the older members perhaps) were not so keen on Munro changes (or indeed any Club changes), some no doubt because they had compleated, or nearly compleated and didn't fancy feeling obliged to top up; others simply viewed the Tables as a sacred cow. Others of course (the younger, more active members) wanted them tidied up to a greater or lesser extent; all very debatable of course but a grudging compromise did let in new ideas. I personally was all for a vigorous sorting out, believing that this is what Munro would have done (and was doing) as new evidence, on the maps (and with your eyes!) became known. And today, all the changes are in place – a very good example of a British progression, whatever the topic, involving changes and improvements.

'In conclusion, let me say that I look back upon the days I have spent in pursuing this quest as among the best spent days of my life'. Those are the words of A E Robertson. That is what it is all about. The list may always be changing but, doing so, also implies it is never changing, and anyway, the Munros will happily outlast Munro-ing.

Chapter 3

Organising the Heightings

Iain A. Robertson

The events have become known as 'The Heightings', with a capital aitch. The word is borrowed from the Surveying Trade, not the part that guesses the value of property, but the part which measures things on the ground. When setting about measuring the height of something, a Heighting is being undertaken. The verb "to height" hovers on the horizon, but has possibly yet to arrive in dictionaries. Were there an English language equivalent of the *Académie française,* much time and effort would no doubt be devoted to the legitimacy of these variations, but fortunately the English language evolves unhindered.

The question posed by 914m emerged when the Ordnance Survey (OS) went metric in c.1974. The metric equivalent of 3,000ft is 914.4m and, given the latitude in height measurements allowed for by the OS, then a mountain marked as 914m could be over 3,000 ft. There were two such mountains within the area covered by *Munro's Tables,* Beinn Dearg (Torridon) and the Ganu Mòr of Foinaven; both were classed as Corbetts. Speculation waxed and waned over the years but the matter remained unresolved until 2006, when it was put to The Munro Society (TMS) Executive that the matter should be settled once and for all and the organisation to undertake such an investigation should be TMS. So far so good, but how to accurately measure the height of a mountain? Personal GPS devices were in use by this time, but were known to be not sufficiently accurate in vertical measurement. Fortunately, there was a TMS member, David Bunting, a retired military surveyor, who advised that there were indeed highly accurate devices which could do the job, but these were extremely expensive and required expertise to operate; moreover, a commercial contract to carry out a measurement would be well beyond the resources of TMS. The use of such devices was, however, a prerequisite to any height adjustments being accepted by the OS, and the Scottish Mountaineering Club (SMC), which is the custodian of *Munro's Tables,* would not accept any height amendments unless verified by the OS. So, if the project was to proceed on a sound footing, means had to be found to reduce the cost.

At that juncture, it appeared that a considerable portion of the overall cost would be the time professional surveyors spent on the mountain. But this, it was thought, could be reduced if TMS members took the equipment to a summit, pressed the necessary button(s) and then brought the equipment back for the professionals to do the clever bits. In this spirit of naïve optimism some four surveying firms were approached to see if they would reduce the price of a survey if TMS members did the leg-work. Of the four firms approached, two did not reply but two, while making it quite clear they would not let TMS members near their expensive machines, were prepared to do a survey at no cost in view of the consequent publicity. The first surveying firm to reply was CMCR Ltd. of Larbert, which was prepared to survey both mountains, and its offer was accepted. The financial problem was thus solved. In practice TMS members did do much of the leg-work, for part of the deal was that the surveyors and their equipment

Above: The southern ridge of Foinaven (Bill Taylor)

Below: Press Conference at Falkirk Golf Club: Iain A. Robertson, President TMS; David Corfield, CEO CMCR Ltd.; Graham Little, representing the Ordnance Survey; and Jim Melville, Project Surveyor (TMS Archive)

should be safely conveyed to the summits and back again.

The first TMS Heightings were conducted over the spring and summer of 2007. There were in fact three expeditions as the weather was so bad on Beinn Dearg, the first Heighting, that the party had to turn back before reaching the summit. Adverse weather was, unfortunately, to be a characteristic of many future Heightings. The schedule for climbing Foinaven was such that a return to Beinn Dearg was not possible beforehand and so the first completed Heighting was Foinaven, on 12th May 2007. TMS members were quite accustomed to the vagaries of the Scottish weather, but the Surveyors, Jim Melville and Evangelos Pentzas, who was an apprentice surveyor from Greece, are to be commended in getting themselves half way up Beinn Dearg and all the way up Foinaven. Many TMS members took the opportunity to be involved in these additional events and the Heightings expeditions were similar in the spirit of camaraderie characteristic of other TMS hill trips.

CMCR Ltd. organised the publicity side and the first Joint CMCR/TMS Press Conference to announce the Foinaven result was held on 8th June 2007 at Falkirk Golf Club. The smart money had been on a new Munro, but in fact Foinaven was found to be 911.0m (2,988.9ft), nearly 11ft lower than the previous map height. This height difference, along with that on Beinn Dearg Mòr in 2011, were the two greatest divergences from previously recorded heights of all the Heightings. Graham Little, Operations Manager for Scotland, OS, was present at the Press Conference to give official approval to the new height. There had been considerable interest prior to the event which was well covered in all the media. Perhaps the most amusing was John Humphrys' interview with Irvine Butterfield (First President of TMS) on the BBC Radio 4 'Today' programme when he tried to wheedle Irvine into an early divulgence of the result, but Irvine was giving nothing away. The, perhaps, saddest tale, which is also one of the funniest, concerned Gavin Madeley, a reporter for the *Daily Mail*, who had the ingenious idea of climbing Foinaven on the morning of 8th June (which he did) in order to be the first person to climb the new Munro!

Beinn Dearg was heighted on 25th August in indifferent weather. Evangelos Pentzas had returned to Greece to do his military National Service and on this occasion Jim Melville was accompanied by Liam Hill, also of CMCR Ltd. The Joint Press Conference to announce the result was again held at Falkirk Golf Club, on 7th September 2007. Media interest was good, but perhaps inevitably, was less on this second occasion. The fact that Beinn Dearg retained its Corbett status, 913.6m (2,997.6ft) almost certainly reduced the actual coverage.

Mission accomplished; but there appeared at the time to be, certainly on the part of CMCR Ltd., an appetite for further publicity-generating Heightings. From TMS' point of view, no pattern of variations had emerged from the two Heightings undertaken, but the discrepancy of almost eleven feet between the previous OS height and that determined by CMCR Ltd. on Foinaven appeared to justify further investigation of mountains clustered above and below 3,000ft. A list of possible contenders was produced in September 2007.

Munros listed at 915m	**Corbett listed at 913m**
Sgùrr nan Ceannaichean	Sgùrr a' Choire-bheithe
Ben Vane	**Corbetts listed at 912m**
Beinn Teallach	Beinn Bhreac
Munros listed at 916m	Leathad an Taobhain (trig point)
Beinn a' Chlèibh	**Corbett listed at 911m**
Beinn a' Chlaidheimh	The Fara
Munros listed at 917m	**Corbetts listed at 910m**
Geal-charn (Drumochter)	Meall Buidhe (Glen Lyon)
Càrn Aosda	Beinn Dearg Mòr
Munros listed at 918m	**Corbetts listed at 909m**
Sgùrr a' Mhadaidh	Beinn nan Oighreag
Ruadh Stac Mòr (trig point)	Leum Uilleim
Meall na Teanga	Streap
Creag nan Damh	
A' Ghlas-bheinn	

It was recognised from the outset that the mountains at either extremity of the list were unlikely to be heighted, but their eligibility for heighting would become apparent when and if a pattern of variation emerged. Bearing in mind the availability and fitness of the surveyors, four further phases of Heightings were drawn up, each phase to correspond with a summer season.

Phase II   Sgùrr nan Ceannaichean, Ben Vane, Beinn Teallach, Beinn a' Chlèibh and Sgùrr a' Choire-bheithe

Phase III   The three Fisherfield mountains (Beinn a' Chlaidheimh, Beinn Dearg Mòr and Ruadh Stac Mòr), the two Gaick mountains (Beinn Bhreac and Leathad an Taobhain), Càrn Aosda and Geal-charn (Drumochter)

Phase IV   The two Kintail mountains (A' Ghlas-bheinn and Creag nan Damh), the Fara, Meall na Teanga, Sgùrr a' Mhadaidh and Meall Buidhe (Glen Lyon Corbett)

Phase V   Beinn nan Oighreag, Leum Uilleim and Streap

As will become apparent, it was not found possible to stick precisely to this ordering.

A copy of the list and the phases was passed to CMCR Ltd. for its information and comment. The reply, in January 2008, was favourable but contained a catch which TMS perhaps should have seen coming rather sooner, CMCR Ltd. were no longer willing to provide its services free of charge. To be fair, it had quoted charges 'at a lower rate than normal to emphasise the spirit of co-operation that thus far existed between the Munro Society and CMCR Ltd.' Nonetheless, of the five quotations submitted, the cheapest was Beinn a' Chlèibh at £1,400 excluding VAT and the most expensive Sgùrr a' Choire-bheithe at £2,200 excluding VAT; surveyors' accommodation costs would be in addition. These were sums which far exceeded the resources of TMS, which CMCR Ltd. may or may not have surmised in advance; whatever the case, the Heightings could not continue if TMS was to be the sole source of funds.

After further consideration, however, a possible additional source of funds was identified in the form of the Scottish Mountaineering Trust (SMT), which is the recipient of profits from the sale of SMC publications. It was decided to modify Phase II to two Heightings: Ben Vane and Beinn Teallach, and an application for the total cost of these two Heightings plus VAT (£3,525), was submitted to the SMT. The application was made in February 2008, but there was no decision from the SMT until July 2008. A grant of £350 was awarded. In reply TMS thanked the SMT for the grant but, as the award was so small a proportion of the sum required and no other sources were known 'for such a singular project', the grant was not taken up. CMCR Ltd. had been kept informed of the grant application and the modified Phase II, but there were no further attempts to attract grants and the door to employing commercial surveyors was closed and has since remained so. Relations with CMCR Ltd. remained friendly and it was 'kept in the loop' regarding further developments until, after a change of name (Survey First Ltd.), the company ceased trading.

By July 2008 it appeared that Heightings conducted by TMS were at an end; expensive equipment and experts to operate the machines and analyse the results were well beyond what the Society could afford, even on a reduced commercial basis. But in fact, the Heightings were about to enter their most productive period.

During 2008 there was a press report about three *hobbyist* surveyors who had established that a Welsh Mountain, Mynydd Graig Goch, previously on the maps as being less than 2,000ft, in fact exceeded 2,000ft, thus giving it official 'Welsh mountain' status. The

A new Welsh mountain – Mynydd Graig Goch (©Myrddyn Phillips)

Mynydd Graig Goch – the surveyors with BBC film crew and John Craven of 'Countryfile'
(©Myrddyn Phillips)

measurements had been accepted by the OS. There was to be a Press Conference to officially mark this change in height (changes in height appear to give rise to Press Conferences) and Fred Ward, the then TMS Treasurer, was invited to attend. Fred met the said hobbyist surveyors: John Barnard and Graham Jackson, and also their associate, Myrddyn Phillips. Fortuitously, both John and Graham had already climbed all the Munros and were thus eligible for TMS membership, which they took up. There was sufficient interest on both sides at this initial meeting in Wales for a more formal meeting to take place in Kendal on 18th November 2008.

At Kendal it was agreed, subject to ratification by TMS Executive, that Graham and John or G & J Surveys, as they later called themselves, would undertake Heightings on behalf of TMS at costs between £500 and £600 per Heighting, depending on the location; TMS members would be asked to help carry the equipment. Further discussions ensued as to certain items within the overall cost figure and the upshot was that G & J Surveys would, on a trial basis, undertake two consecutive Heightings during one trip to Scotland at an estimated cost of £830; in the event the bill to cover their costs was £775. The mountains to be heighted were Beinn Teallach and Ben Vane. It was also agreed that it would be unnecessary to involve the OS unless the Heighting suggested a change in Munro/Corbett status or if there was a 'significant' variation in height – as had been the case with Foinaven. Beinn Teallach was heighted on 15th May 2009 and Ben Vane on 16th May 2009. In neither case was there a significant change in height from the previous OS figure and the Munros status of the two mountains was confirmed.

Left: John Barnard with the Leica NA730 automatic level (Iain A. Robertson)

Above: Graham Jackson with the Leica Viva GS15 GNSS receiver (©Myrddyn Phillips)

The weather was not kind; fortunately, the entire party, including the surveyors, were familiar with Scottish weather and had the necessary gear, but Beinn Teallach was battered by winds gusting up to 70 mph according to the surveyors' anemometer and there is a picture of the summit party failing to keep upright for a photograph. Ben Vane was less windy but there was thick mist and rain. Ben Vane was busy with other walkers making their way to the cairn; it was a Saturday. When it was pointed out that it had just been established that the cairn was not on the highest point, which was some yards off in the mist, I observed no one going to the actual top. Is there something about cairns?

There was a further unexpected development during 2009. TMS member, the late Clem Clements, very generously donated the sum of money necessary to cover the cost of heighting Sgùrr a' Choire-bheithe above Barisdale. This was to celebrate the fortieth anniversary of Clem's compleation on nearby Ladhar Bheinn. Sgùrr a' Choire-bheithe was of course the highest un-heighted Corbett and one of the strongest contenders to be heighted. In order to take advantage of the Surveyors' journey north, it was decided that they should undertake a further Heighting, funded by the Society, and the Munro, Sgùrr nan Ceannaichean, was selected as it was the remaining 915m mountain and it was not too far from Ratagan Youth Hostel where the Barisdale party was staying. The fast boat service from Arnisdale to Barisdale was operating in 2009 and this greatly assisted getting the Heighting Party to Barisdale and back within a day. There was a thick, wet mist, but it was relatively mild. The weather was better in Glen Carron the next day and some good views were enjoyed from the summit of Sgùrr nan Ceannaichean while the readings were being recorded.

TMS had remained tight-lipped about the results of all four 2009 Heightings in the belief that one big announcement would generate more interest than four individual ones. But after the Sgùrr nan Ceannaichean Heighting, there was yet more of interest – a change of status. The final Heighting of the year, after confirmation by the OS, found that Sgùrr nan Ceannaichean, at 913.5m, had reverted to its previous status of Corbett, having been moved from Corbett to Munro in 1981. TMS Executive decided that a change of status was sufficient reason for a Press Conference which was to take place on 10th September 2009. To heighten the interest (pun intended), the names of the four mountains heighted during the year were made widely known as was the fact that one would change status, but which one and what change of status? This certainly gave rise to comment and speculation among the hill-going public and the redoubtable Dave Hewitt, of *The Angry Corrie* fame, endeavoured to introduce an element of controversy into the proceedings, but that is what journalists are supposed to do.

In the event, the Press Conference was poorly attended by the media, but the actual coverage on radio and in the press, was satisfactory, including a slightly jokey editorial in *Scotland on Sunday* of 13th September 2009. The SMC had (in confidence) been previously informed of the reduction in height of Sgùrr nan Ceannaichean and its representatives attended the Press Conference. In addition to a hand-out explaining the SMC's role as custodian of *Munro's Tables*, they had with them a printer's proof of the new entry in The Corbetts, guidebook covering the re-classified Sgùrr nan Ceannaichean, an impressive effort.

The case for TMS to continue with its programme of Heightings was reinforced by the reclassification of Sgùrr nan Ceannaichean and the Executive endorsed a provisional programme for 2010 which again involved the surveyors coming north, this time on two occasions, and conducting three Heightings on the first occasion and two on the second. The group of three consisted of The Fara, Geal-charn (Drumochter) and Beinn Bhreac; the first two were adjacent to the A9, but the latter was in Gaick, beyond Bruar Lodge. The group of two was much more dispersed: Beinn a' Chlèibh and Leathad an Taobhain, also in Gaick, but best approached from Glen Feshie. It was thought that heighting the two Gaick Corbetts would be greatly assisted if the surveying gear could be taken part of the way by a four-wheel drive vehicle. Application was made to Glen Feshie Estate and Atholl Estates for leave to use such vehicles; permission was ultimately granted in both cases, but neither could be accommodated that year prior to the stalking season. The modified pro-gramme which ensued was Geal-charn on 16th April 2010, followed by Beinn a' Chlèibh, 30th July 2010, and The Fara, 31st July 2010.

On Geal-charn the party enjoyed the best weather of all the Heightings. The sun shone all day and it was a pleasure to sit round the cairn or walk out to the adjacent A' Mharconaich. Jim Melville, who had carried out the first two Heightings in 2007, was one of the party on this occasion. The height, however, remained at 917m and the Munro status confirmed. No change also applied to Beinn a' Chlèibh, heighted in appallingly wet and windy weather, and the Fara, in an occasionally dispersing mist. An interesting fact did, however, emerge from the investigation of The Fara. Those familiar with the summit will recall that there is an enormous cairn which is the start/finish of a stone dyke; this was assumed to mark the summit. Large cairns are a problem in heighting for the measurements must be from a fixed part of the mountain, i.e. not

Above: Geal-charn from the south (Iain A. Robertson)

Below: Beinn a' Chlèibh (Derek Sime)

Above: The Fara from Beinn Udlamain (David Batty)

Below: Enjoying the sun on Geal-charn, Myrddyn Phillips, Jim Melville, David Batty, Peter Willimott, Charles Murray, Eleanore Hunter and David Cran. (Iain A Robertson)

a loose boulder. Cairns consist of loose boulders and so on occasions cairns have to be dismantled (and replaced) in order to find a fixed point. Dismantling The Fara cairn was a daunting prospect. In doing the job properly however, John, Graham and Myrddyn always did a survey of the ground when the top was flat, to unambiguously identify the highest point; visual observation is insufficient. On this occasion, they found that a rock tor, some 100m SSW of the cairn, was the highest point, though at 911.4m not high enough for a change in status, and so the cairn remained intact.

The year 2010 had been one of confirmation with no changes in status or significant alterations in height. TMS Executive might have been looking seriously at whether further heighting expenditures were justified had there not been an unexpected development. Quite early in that year, the Heightings Co-ordinator had received an e-mail from TMS member Alan Haworth, Lord Haworth of Fisherfield. This contained an offer to finance the Heighting of three mountains in the Fisherfield Forest, namely Beinn a' Chlaidheimh, Beinn Dearg Mòr and Ruadh Stac Mòr, all of which were on the List of Contenders drawn up in 2007. This was an offer that could not be refused and so during 2010, those involved in planning and organising the Heightings knew that there would be another season to organise the following year.

Lord Haworth of Fisherfield approaches the summit of Beinn Dearg Mòr
(Iain A. Robertson)

Its remoteness is one of the great attractions of the Fisherfield Forest, but remoteness also posed difficulties for the movement of persons and equipment and the Surveyors estimated a five-day allowance to cover three Heightings; an estimate which proved accurate. Two alternative approaches were considered: to operate from a base in Strath na Sealga which was central, but not equidistant from the three mountains, or to mount three separate lightweight expeditions from an exterior base. Initially, the first alternative looked the more attractive. Hiring a helicopter to ferry the Surveyors (not others) and their equipment in and out was costed, but this would have taken most of Alan Haworth's generous £3,000 grant and was rejected on this and other grounds. An alternative was to carry in tents and supplies for a five-day stay by a (then) unknown number of people. Use of a four-wheel drive vehicle might have made this more feasible, but this proved a non-starter. Using Shenavall was rejected as inappropriate use of a bothy. Three separate expeditions began to look the most sensible option and this was the final choice. All sixteen beds at the Sàil Mhòr hostel were booked for five nights from Sunday 3rd July 2011.

From the time of the Foinaven Heighting back in 2007, there had been approaches from media professionals, film and print, to be permitted to accompany a Heighting expedition. These had never been rejected, though it had always been made clear that

Beinn a' Chlaidheimh from Ruadh Stac Mòr (Iain A. Robertson)

such individuals would be entirely responsible for their own transport and welfare. This was the case with a film company and a reporter prior to Fisherfield, but, as in all previous and future occasions they did not turn up. The only filming during Heightings was done by Myrddyn Phillips with a digi-camcorder, apart from the occasion when TMS was asked to stage a 'Heighting' for a German TV company, of which more anon.

The Fisherfield Heightings proved very popular with TMS members; all the places at Sàil Mhòr were taken, two were in an adjacent B & B and two camped above Achneigie. It must be said that this was not entirely due to enthusiasm to carry measuring equipment, there was an ulterior motive among some to pick off the Strath na Sealga Corbetts – and why not?

Three long strenuous days were in prospect and, if memory serves, only John, Graham and Myrddyn were involved in all three. Others made themselves available for one or two days out of the three. The Monday was devoted to Beinn a' Chlaidheimh, walking in from Corrie Hallie. It was warm and windless, but with good visibility and the team worked hard to get themselves and the gear to the top. However, all went well and they returned to a prepared meal. Tribute should be paid here to those TMS members, Glen Breaden in particular, who saw to it that there was a meal ready when a team returned from a hard day's Heighting. The Tuesday was an off day and the best for weather during the entire week. Some members appropriately climbed Sàil Mhòr. Wednesday was Beinn Dearg Mòr and a full turnout, including Alan Haworth. Again, the walk was from Corrie Hallie and over the shoulder of An Teallach to Shenevall. The rivers were low and so the walk round to the south side of the mountain was straightforward, though the party was somewhat strung-out by that time. The weather was grey with mist occasionally covering the top of Beinn Dearg Mòr. The large summit cairn problem re-appeared but was surmounted and most of the stragglers eventually reached the summit, some via Beinn Dearg Bheag. It was nearly 23:00 hours before everyone had reported back to Sàil Mhòr Hostel. Thursday was a rest day and as Friday was to be another big day, an additional night's accommodation was booked for those likely to be involved on the Friday.

The final Heighting was Ruadh Stac Mòr, which was best approached from the south. John Barnard successfully negotiated with Letterewe Estate and permission was granted to take cars as far as Kernsary, which saved about 6km of walking. Nonetheless, it was a long day. The weather was generally kind and stayed clear, although there were brief rain showers. Sitting around on the tops of mountains for two hours or more which a Heighting involved was not always a comfortable experience, but the two hours spent on Ruadh Stac Mòr were among the best this writer has enjoyed on the hills. Fisherfield Forest was spread out before us with Beinn Dearg and the Fannichs clear beyond. A soft shower of rain gave rise to a brilliant rainbow located below our vantage point; it was a privilege to be there. The return journey was wearisome, enlivened near the end by clouds of ferocious midges, but the job was done.

It had been anticipated that there would be no significant change in the height of Ruadh Stac Mòr as it had a trig point, and this was the case. Beinn Dearg Mòr lost no less than 4m falling from 910m to 906.4m, which was disappointing as there had been hopes of a 'new' Munro. The significant change was to Beinn a' Chlaidheimh which, though only a marginal change, dropped below 914.4m to 914.0m which implied a reversion to its original, pre-1974, status of Corbett. All the findings were accepted by the OS.

In the immediate aftermath of Fisherfield, Alan Haworth had been consulting with some of his media acquaintances at Westminster about the most effective way of making a further alteration to *Munro's Tables* widely known, should that become necessary. The previous Press Conference had been expensive and ill-attended. In particular, Alan spoke to Mike Elrick, an expert in this area, who also had compleated the Munros. Elrick's advice was to issue a Press Release via the internet which should include a 'phone number if further details were required. The implied change in status for Beinn a' Chlaidheimh clearly required information about TMS's role in undertaking the Heighting, and a Press Release was decided upon. The date for the Press Release was fixed for 9th August 2011 at 09:00 hours. This duly went ahead and was very successful in its coverage. It did, however, create something of a hiatus which was not of TMS's making. The SMC had been kept fully informed of the Heightings and the new heights, as accepted by the OS. Prior to the issue of the Press release, of which the SMC had been fully informed, it asked for the following brief statement to be included:

> The Scottish Mountaineering Club has been notified of these survey results and has undertaken to consider the implications for Munro's and Corbett's Tables when the Ordnance Survey updates its map of the area.

The only 'implication' was Beinn a' Chlaidheimh being found to be less than 914.4m, which to many appeared a fact rather than an implication. The hill-walking interest had been aware that Heightings had taken place in July and the word had spread that there had been changes in heights, but not which mountains or in which direction. The Press Release was awaited with interest, and subsequently the position adopted by the SMC, as Custodians of *Munro's Tables*, was widely regarded as being indecisive and confusing.

TMS offered no opinion or comment on the matter, though it did subsequently issue the following clarification on how the OS dealt with alterations to maps:

> We are informed that the OS updates its 1:25,000 digital data twice a year in May and October so the changes [regarding Fisherfield] will follow in October 2011; the 1:50,000 digital data is updated once a year in June so the changes will be in June 2012. From these dates onwards any custom maps ordered through 'OS Select' will show the new heights.

The following appeared on the SMC website in September 2012:

> And then there were 282… Following confirmation that the Ordnance Survey has adopted the height information from last year's independent survey of Beinn a' Chlaidheimh, The Scottish Mountaineering Club can confirm that, at 914m, the mountain falls short of the 914.4m height required to be considered a Munro.

Returning to the coverage obtained by the Press Release, this was very successful, particularly in the press, with the Press Association Report appearing in some forty-two newspapers, in addition to individual reports in the larger dailies. For the first time the Heightings were mentioned in foreign newspapers: *The Wall Street Journal* of 29th July 2011 mentioned the Heighting process but not the result; the Heighting and the result was given in the English language edition of a Croatian newspaper. Dare one say, 'it must have been a slack day for news in Croatia'?

The first tentative plans for 2012 were for two visits by the Surveyors over the summer. The first was to height the two Gaick Corbetts, Leathad an Taobhain and Beinn Bhreac, which had been held over from 2010. The second sortie north was primarily at the Surveyors' own initiative and it was to check the status of Knight's Peak on Sgùrr nan Gillean, which at the time was recorded as a Munro Top. As they were to be in Skye, however, it was thought that Sgùrr a' Mhadaidh, which was on the original List of Contenders, might also be heighted under TMS sponsorship.

The arrangements for Gaick went forward smoothly; permission to use four-wheel vehicles on estate roads was forthcoming from both Atholl Estates and the Glen Feshie Estate. At this point the Society's debt to Anne and Bill Butler for the use of their Range Rover is acknowledged. On Glen Feshie Estate the excellent road system allowed the vehicle to be driven up on to the plateau as far as Meall an Uilt

Climbing the hard way, the Butler Range Rover, Leathad an Taobhain behind (Iain A. Robertson)

Chreagaich, only a short distance from Leathad an Taobhain. On Atholl Estates this was driven as far as Bruar Lodge; other members of the party cycled to this point. Bicycles were used also on this occasion, to the detriment of at least one bike. The party stayed at the SMC Raeburn Hut near Dalwhinnie, which was reasonably near both hills. As was more usually the case, the weather was not propitious for either day's Heighting. Rain, wind and thick mist sums it all up and the beauties of Gaick were unobserved. As had been anticipated, the height of Leathad an Taobhain coincided almost exactly with the Flush Bracket height on the trig point and Beinn Bhreac remained a good 2m short of Munro status. No change removed the necessity of any public announcement, though the findings were passed to the SMC.

The role of Heightings Co-ordinator, as it came to be called, had been undertaken by Iain Robertson since the first Heightings in 2007. Before the start of the 2012 season he had asked that someone else take over the role and it had been agreed that he organise the Gaick Heightings and then hand over to his successor, Alistair Milner. Unfortunately, illness prevented Alistair organising a second Heighting in 2012.

By 2013 it had become apparent to the TMS Executive that the pattern of results which had emerged from the Heightings indicated that there was little if any likelihood of the heights of the remaining Munros or Corbetts on the List of Contenders being significantly inaccurate in terms of change of status. This was not, however, quite the end. The Surveyors were still keen to height Knight's Peak, to which had been added the Bhàsteir Tooth, also a Munro Top. A jointly funded expedition to Skye was thus organised by Alistair Milner during the summer of 2013. On both Heightings, members of the SMC assisted with ropes at the more exposed sections. It was found that Knight's Peak was marginally less than 914.4m and it has since ceased to be listed as a Munro Top; the Bhàsteir Tooth was confirmed in its status of Munro Top.

It appeared to TMS members that the Skye Heightings of 2013 would be the end of a most enjoyable, but inevitably finite series of events; certainly so, in regard to Munro/ Corbett status and, with the two Skye exceptions, the Executive had decided against investigating marginal Munro Tops. The Surveyors: John and Graham, and their associate Myrddyn, had also found the expeditions enjoyable and no doubt the TMS work helped to establish G & J Survey's reputation in the Heighting field. Be that as it may, as a gesture of thanks they very generously offered to undertake an additional Heighting on a mountain chosen by TMS and at no cost to TMS. The past Heightings Co-ordinator was given the honour of choosing the mountain.

Choosing a worthwhile Heighting was not easy; it had to be a situation where a height measurement was crucial, but Munro/Corbett was now done and checking existing Munro Tops had been set aside. Checking the marginal Corbetts/Grahams was a possibility, but what would be really exciting would be something altogether new. This writer, and others, was aware that in the Monadhliath Mountains, there was an outlying top lying some 5km south-west of the Munro, Carn Dearg, which, at 834m, was above the 762m necessary for Corbett status. It is called Marg na Craige (NN621973). Corbetts, in addition to the height stipulation, also have a drop stipulation of at least 500ft (152.4m). In terms of Marg na Craige, this meant that the lowest point between Carn Dearg and Marg na Craige had to be no higher than (834-152.4 =) 681.6m. A study

Above: North ridge of Meall Gaineimh from Glen Avon (Iain A. Robertson)

Below: The Tor, Meall Gaineimh (Iain A. Robertson)

of the map indicated that the lowest point lies north of Meallan Dubh (NH614001), on the watershed between the burns flowing south-west into Glen Markie and those flowing south-east into Glen Banchor. Two visits to Meallan Dubh and a study of the drainage pattern indicated that the lowest point must be a particular small lochan. Reference to a small-scale map showed, however, a spot height adjacent to the lochan was 10m too high. So, no new Corbett; the Surveyors may well have breathed a sigh of relief for checking the *lowest* point on a boggy bealach would have been time-consuming if nothing else.

The other strong possibility, suggested by others, was of an entirely new Munro Top on Ben Avon, and this was the Heighting ultimately chosen. The Top was Meall Gaineimh (NJ167053) some 4km north-east of the summit of Ben Avon. The possibility arose because, although there was a cairn on the highest part of the plateau of Meall Gaineimh which may have been the OS Heighting point, there was a higher granite tor adjacent to the west. A good representative number of the old Heighting Gang, with representatives from the SMC, joined the expedition which stayed in the Tomintoul Hostel. The Surveyors had contacted the Balmoral Estate and permission was given to take cars up the estate road so far, and the Butler Range Rover to not far short of the Don/Avon watershed. The day was dull but largely clear of mist and the party reached the plateau from Inchrory by a system of tracks. No doubt it was worth the effort and the day was enjoyed by all, but the tor on Meall Gaineimh did not reach 914.4m.

By way of a coda, those TMS and SMC members who had attended at Tomintoul were invited to a similar 'Munro Top investigation' on Carn na Caim, this organised entirely by John, Graham and Myrddyn, though the matter had been previously investigated by Alan Dawson. The top to be investigated was Carn na Caim South Top (also known as Mullach Coire Cisteachan). This is on the plateau which is accessed by the track from the A9. Again, there was a good turnout of the faithful, all of whom had driven up for

The team at the top of Carn na Caim: Bill Wheeler, John Rogerson, Eleanore Hunter, Alan Brook, Rab Anderson, Andy Nisbet, Ian Collie, Graham Jackson, David Batty, John Barnard, Iain Robertson (©Myrddyn Phillips)

the day. It was fairly typical Heighting weather and there is a distinct lack of shelter on the Carn na Caim plateau; only the hardiest stayed for both Heightings, i.e. the top and the drop, but it has now been accepted by the SMC as a new Munro Top, though it is but a bump on the plateau.

To continue the musical simile; the coda had been Mullach Coire Cisteachan and a coda should mark the end of the work. But what if an encore is demanded? During July 2015, a German TV Production Company[1] came to Scotland to make a documentary about aspects of Scottish life and culture.[2] The emphasis was, apparently, to be on the idiosyncratic. How any group of persons who climbed mountains because they were above a certain height and, moreover, went to great lengths to check these heights, could be regarded as idiosyncratic is difficult to fathom. Nevertheless, TMS was approached and asked if it would co-operate in producing a short film about its activities. Whether the Germans had prior knowledge of Heightings or whether that particular activity was suggested to them, this writer is unaware; whatever the case, the plan was they would film a Heighting. But not of course a *real* Heighting, which would take hours and be very boring, but a *pretend* Heighting made lifelike with Surveyors and equipment. It all had to be done in a day and the day had to be fixed in advance which, given the history of the Heightings, meant it would be wet and horrible. Ben Lomond had been suggested as a location, but the party actually met up in the Ben Lawers car park on 28th July 2015. The Germans were intrigued by the anecdote which tells of a former Marquis of Breadalbane who had a 16ft cairn built on Ben Lawers which raised its height to 4,000ft. The Cairn subsequently collapsed. The three Germans were very professional and coped with the weather and also understanding what all the palaver was about – probably. What German TV audiences made of it is another matter. The party marched a short distance up Beinn Ghlas, being filmed en route, and then marched back down again. A scene with poles and Heighting equipment was then staged. It rained most of the time. A donation was made to TMS funds.

And so, what had begun in 2007 as an exercise to check the heights of two Scottish 914m mountains ended in 2015 on German TV. In the opinion of this writer, TMS in organising the Heightings undertook a worthwhile exercise in pursuit of accuracy, and in so doing followed in the footsteps of Hugh Munro and his fellow SMC members who also sought accuracy in terms of the technology of their times. Most who participated in the Heightings nurtured a hope that a new Munro might emerge, but heigh-ho, that was not to be. The point which was reinforced in all our minds was that the quality of a mountain is innate, and has nothing to do with man-made categories. TMS revived the practice of checking heights of Scottish mountains and in so doing made use of the latest technology. It can fairly claim to have measured the most prominent of those mountains requiring attention and has now called a halt to such activities. Others have now followed suit and there are other worthwhile Heighting projects to be investigated by those with access to greater resources than those available to TMS. All such activities lead to more accurate information. Those who participated in the TMS Heightings may take satisfaction from a job well done.

---

1   SWR Fernsehen, a German regional television channel in the states of Baden-Württemberg and Rhineland-Palatinate, produced by Südwestrundfunk (SWR).

2   This was part of a series of programmes entitled 'Länder Menschen Abenteuer' which translates as 'Countries, People, Adventures'.

Above: German TV crew and the Heighting team in the Ben Lawers area (©Myrddyn Phillips)

Below: Filming on the slopes of Beinn Ghlas (Lawers) (©Myrddyn Phillips)

Chapter 4

The First Heightings – Reflections

Derek Sime and Glen Breaden

The First Planned Heighting : Beinn Dearg (Torridon) – Derek Sime

The Heightings programme began in April 2007 with a planned Heighting of Beinn Dearg in Torridon. Beinn Dearg, the blood-red hill of Torridonian sandstone, had long attracted speculation as to its true height, being shown as 914m on the OS maps. In particular, Chris Townsend had previously climbed it and taken hand-held GPS readings, but of course the accuracy of such readings was in no way sufficient for a determination that would satisfy the OS. Given his interest in the matter, Chris accompanied the team over the weekend.

The plan was to survey it on Saturday 21st April. The surveyors were Jim Melville and Evangelos Pentzas of CMCR Ltd., and the party duly assembled at Newton Cottage at Annat on the Friday evening, as guests of the Grampian Club, some of whose members were present. However, the weather forecast was not good, with 'ferocious gusts' of 70mph plus. (Current advice from Mountaineering Scotland in their Wind Speeds webpage for 70mph states: 'You're having a laugh! Seriously though, folks, if you are seeing a wind speed of 70 mph or more on the mountain forecast, this is the time to head for a walk in the glen.' – all the more impressive then that a later Heighting, that on Beinn Teallach, was successfully carried out in just these conditions).

Duly put off by that, it was decided that to attempt a first Heighting in such conditions would not be a good idea, and most headed instead up the coast from Diabaig for a low level walk to the former Youth Hostel, and by then MBA bothy, at Craig, trusting that the weather on the following day would be significantly better. Better being a relative term, it could be argued that indeed it was, with a lighter wind, but with a cloud base of 300-400m, very poor visibility and rain later in the day. Undaunted, we set off from the Coire MhicNòbaill car park at 08:30, a time which proved to be too late considering the very slow pace (one of the two surveyors had never been on a hill before), and the amount of work required at the summit. We continued up to Bealach a' Chòmhla and Suileagan Bhealach up to NG886619 (at approximately 580m). After 3 hours 50 minutes (it was by then 12:20), and with deteriorating weather, it became clear that to continue would probably have meant returning well after dark, and with general concern among the participants, the only sensible course of action was to retreat.

It was therefore something of an abortive mission, with nothing to show for our efforts over the weekend, and although disappointing, it did provide very useful information for future attempts at heighting, not least that the slow pace, and the time required for surveying, necessitated a much earlier start.

Eleanore Hunter has vivid memories of the day –

> I was on seven of the Heightings, including the very first one, back in 2007, on

Beinn Dearg. On that occasion our Heighting Co-ordinator, Iain Robertson was absent for health reasons. In the morning at least one of the older members sped away to the Coire MhicNòbaill car park to get ahead of the main party in order not to be left behind, as he thought. As it happened he need not have worried. While the surveyors from CMCR were eager to carry out this mission, unfortunately Evangelos was not up to speed and in the end was unable to keep walking uphill. The journey had to be aborted and I had been instructed to telephone Iain with the outcome. He could not believe that we had been unable to climb Beinn Dearg! As I had only a basic pay-as-you-go mobile phone, my fear was that the money would run out before I had fully explained the situation. Remember it was 2007. Nowadays there are smart phones and contracts.

The First Successful Heighting : Foinaven, Sutherland – Glen Breaden

It was a significant day for me in more ways than one. But let me turn back awhile: there had been a previously planned, but ultimately aborted attempt to height Beinn Dearg in Torridon. On that occasion the surveyors and load-carrying member volunteers had made their way to Torridon, but foul weather unfortunately put paid to an ascent. Thereafter, there was insufficient time for a second visit before the scheduled Heighting of Foinaven on 12th May 2007

Foinaven, surely one of the most iconic hills of Highland Scotland, was one of those marginally below 3,000ft and thus Munro status. But metrication had apparently reduced the margin and this attracted much debate and speculation down the years, not only regarding its height, but also about the position of the true summit. Whatever, there were many felt it to be *worthy* of Munro status, and I confess to being one such. I was excited about a survey which would finally end all conjecture and in anticipation I looked forward to joining the volunteer group to provide assistance and company for the surveyors (Jim Melville and Evangelos Pentzas) from CMCR Ltd. of Larbert. As it ultimately turned out Foinaven was to be the first of fourteen mountains and two tops to be accurately surveyed over the next decade at the initiative of TMS.

As with all Heightings, it wasn't just a matter of climbing the hill. The necessary and unwieldy equipment had to be carried as well. These loads were distributed among the volunteers and, when necessary, the heavier pieces were exchanged en route. Consideration of time had to be given as the pace would be slow due to the equipment and the fitness level of the two surveyors, unused to tramping up hills. Furthermore once there, the paraphernalia took time to assemble; then a wait of up to three hours as the relevant data were being collected by the instruments. In Foinaven's case the true summit point had also to be ascertained and verified before the equipment was put into place. This meant, as those who have assisted on a Heighting know, that there's a long time spent hanging about on and around the summit, and the weather cannot be predicted when expeditions are fixed weeks in advance.

Inchnadamph Lodge was booked as base camp – an excellent choice given its proximity to Foinaven and its good facilities, although one of the party stayed at the campsite in Scourie, being significantly closer to the planned starting point. It was at Inchnadamph, on the 11th May, that the surveyors and volunteers assembled, settled in, and planned the following day. The forecast looked favourable so we all retired feeling relaxed and confident of attaining our goal – the successful Heighting of Foinaven.

Given the task, the direct route was chosen, that from the A838 in the north-west where there is suitable parking. It is quite a trek over boggy, peaty moorland to reach the base of the hill, but the party was eager, fresh and keen to get on, so my recollection is that we made reasonable time to this point, where we regrouped and made some adjustments to the carrying of equipment. Unfortunately, we were about to enter the mist in which the hill was shrouded. But, as we hardy hill-goers are pretty used to such conditions, we pressed on. The going proved okay, but we made slow progress due to the weight of the equipment and allowance made for less fit surveyors. At length we reached our first landmark, Foinaven's westerly top of Ceann Garbh. The cairn was covered in ice crystals, which looked attractive, but more positively it felt as if the clag was thinning a little. With the less stiff gradient thereafter, and the knowledge that the summit was only another two kilometres ahead, we made better progress. Gaining height once more we entered ever-thickening clag, and so it remained until we reached the summit cairn. The surveyors quickly got on with the job which meant much to-ing and fro-ing in limited visibility establishing what was the true summit point from which to set up their instruments.

Above: The summit cairn on Ceann Garbh (Glen Breaden)

Below: The GPS instrument being set up (Derek Sime)

Even for May month it was exceedingly cold and damp, so rucksacks were raided for all extra and necessary warm clothing. As it would be a long wait, Fred Ward, Walter McArthur and I decided to head east over to another 'summit' cairn which seemed to suddenly appear out of the mist. We cooried doon while unpacking food and thermos flasks. Others headed off south towards a bealach – anything to keep warm!

Suddenly and miraculously one of the delights of hill walking occurred. To the north-east we were tantalised by glimpses of our surroundings, then the veil slowly started to dissipate, as if an unseen hand was lifting it cautiously and deliberately. Oh the wonder and delight of being able to view our splendid surroundings and the further landscapes bathed in sunlight. There were Cranstackie and Beinn Spionnaidh, there was the coast leading our eyes to the Pentland Firth and the Orkney Isles beyond. Slowly turning westwards there was Kinlochbervie and the sparkling Atlantic Ocean, and nearer to hand the surveyors busy working and everyone smiling and giving the thumbs up. Then one of Foinaven's east ridges just beyond the deep and steep Coire nan Lurgainn

came sharply into view, and beyond we caught sight of Foinaven's twin, the shapely Arkle. We were enjoying one of the most spectacular 360° panoramas in Scotland. It was magical. It was thrilling, but above all for me it was truly extraordinary. In my mind's eye I can still see it today as clearly as then. It was an unforgettable experience.

Jim Melville adjusts the gear on Ganu Mòr (Bill Taylor)

After the data had been collected on Foinaven:
(back) Fred Ward, Alf Barnard, Irvine Butterfield, Derek Sime, Angus Campbell, Walter McArthur;
(front) Evangelos Pentzas, Glen Breaden and Jim Melville (Bill Taylor)

However, more importantly, the rising mist raised everyone's spirits, warmed us, and brought out all the cameras. Weren't we fortunate to enjoy the rest of our time on the summit! But time was quickly passing, the surveyors were happy that their work was done, and so with the gear packed up, we began our return walk, which by contrast to the ascent was leisurely and light hearted. The task had been undertaken satisfactorily and our descent eased with the staggeringly beautiful westerly views.

Tired but happy that evening we relaxed over supper and enjoyed a beer or, in some cases, a wee dram or two. The surveyors remained tight-lipped about their findings for it all had to be checked and ratified before being verified and agreed by the OS, after which a formal press announcement was scheduled for the following month.

Why was this day so significant for me? Apart from it being TMS's first Heighting, it was also First President Irvine Butterfield's final hill in our company. He was a sick man, but was still determined to share that day and with much credit he did, albeit with some generous assistance. I shall never forget his wide grin when he made it to the summit. What an achievement for a gentleman who died two years later. Indeed for so many reasons it was a memorable day, added to which it was my birthday!

Success at Last : Beinn Dearg (Torridon) – Derek Sime

After the Foinaven Heighting, the next available date which suited everyone (most of all the surveyors), and when Newton Cottage was free, was in late August, and once again the party assembled there on the Friday evening (24th August), although due to pressure on accommodation in the Cottage, I stayed in the midge-ridden and somewhat basic campsite a mile along the road at Torridon.

Having learned our lesson from the April attempt, and gained experience from the successful Foinaven Heighting, I set the alarm for 4.30 am. Breakfasting in the dark, it felt more reminiscent of setting out to climb a high Alpine summit, except that, rather than the crystal clear star-speckled Alpine night sky, there was the all too familiar low cloud, and continuous drizzle. The voracious Highland midge population was a source of absolute distraction as we set off from the car park at 06:30 and followed more or less the same route we had taken four months earlier, arriving at the summit at 11:30 (no less than five hours after setting out). We had been a little more optimistic about the weather on this occasion, with the forecast reading 25-30mph westerly, gusting to 45, causing considerable buffeting on exposed ridges (if only some of this wind had been present at the car park, and much of the approach walk, to keep the midges at bay).

In the event, the weather was not particularly kind, but bearable, with a cloud base of 500m, clearing for a time in the early afternoon, with frequent drizzle and a west wind. In what was almost a repeat of the Foinaven experience, the mist gradually lifted during our time on the ridge, opening up views of Beinn Alligin (particularly of the Horns), Liathach, Sàil Mhòr and Ruadh Stac Mòr on Beinn Eighe, Beinn an Eòin, Baosbheinn, and the great wilderness of the Shieldaig and Flowerdale Forests, with more distant views of the Fisherfield heights, and, later, as the mist further cleared, the unmistakable bulk of Slioch. The strong gusts in the event did not materialise, and the weather proved to be no obstacle to getting the job done.

The team at the summit after data collection was complete: Patrick Hetherington, Susan Sharpe, Ian Collie, Bob Kyle, Liam Hill (sitting), Findlay Swinton, Eleanore Hunter, Walter McArthur, Angus Campbell (sitting), Peter Willimott, John Ross, Bill Taylor, Fred Ward, Jim Melville (Derek Sime)

The data collection over, and the obligatory photo-calls complete, the equipment was dismantled and distributed among Munro Society 'porters' for the descent, which initially involved retracing steps along the ridge to the bealach between the summit and Stùc Loch na Cabhaig, then down the steep but relatively straightforward grassy slopes to the north-east into An Coire Mòr, continuing down to around 420m to avoid the crags, before contouring round the north side of the hill to re-join the path through Bealach na Chòmhla and back to the car park. Three hours were spent at the summit, and the full day's expedition took 12½ hours, the last of the party arriving back at the car park at 19:00.

Rumour has it that one enthusiastic journalist, determined to get a piece of the action, had driven over the Dirrie More to climb Beinn Dearg and meet the Heighting team. That was of course the Beinn Dearg near Ullapool, which has a height of 1,084m, and was never likely to be a high priority for Heighting!

After the result became known, I wrote an item for the Scottish Mountaineer on the Heighting, entitled *Old Red – New Height?*[1] The Old Red of course referred to the Torridonian sandstone, but 'New Height' it was not. The height was given as 913.675m, or 2,997.58ft, which was very close to the published OS height of 914m, and confirms both the accuracy of the OS height, and the mountain's status as the highest Corbett (although that was subsequently overtaken when Beinn a' Chlaidheimh was heighted, and found to be just short of Munro status, thereby restoring it to its previous Corbett status).

---

1   *Old Red – New Height?* by Derek Sime, published in *The Scottish Mountaineer*, November 2007.

The team descending Beinn Dearg (Derek Sime)

We also had an article published in *The Scots Magazine* on these two Heightings, in the May 2008 edition.[1] The title of the article – 'Measuring the Munros' – was probably inappropriate, since the two hills measured by then were of course both Corbetts, and remained so, but at least it brought the Heighting activity to a wider readership.

---

1   *Measuring the Munros*, by Derek Sime, published in *The Scots Magazine*, New Series, Vol. 168, No. 5, May 2008.

Chapter 5

Introduction to the Science of Height Surveying

John Barnard and Graham Jackson

How it all Began

It was Friday 19th September 2008 and it was 7.15am. We had been on the road for nearly two long hours and were now making our way up a narrow single-track road in the middle of Wales towards a rendezvous. 'Be there for 7.30am and I'll be by my van,' the man from the BBC had said. We were just going to make it in time. As we rounded a bend in the road the meeting place came into view. Instead of a small van there was a whole fleet of vans within a forest of masts, big vans and little vans and trucks and all from numerous radio stations and television channels. Our contact appeared amid the confusion. 'You're just in time for the first interview,' he said. We looked at each other as he continued, 'The first interview is in three minutes so just relax. There are six million people waiting to hear what you have to say.' No pressure then! We were just announcing to the world that Wales had a new mountain, Mynydd Graig Goch.

Let's go back a few months. Since 2006 we had carried out several surveys in England and Wales where we measured the drop of 2,000ft mountains described in the guide books of John and Anne Nuttall. Measuring a drop of 15m, or even 30m, by a line survey is easy, but measuring a drop of 150m, the criterion for Marilyns, is just impracticable by this technique. Moreover, we had no way of measuring accurately 'absolute' heights. Consequently, one of us went away and did some research and learnt that GPS technology might do the trick. We had even discovered that The Munro Society had carried out two surveys with the help of a surveying company by the name of CMCR Ltd. What was unclear was just how good the technique really was. Accordingly, we contacted Leica GeoSystems and were introduced to James Whitworth. After several conversations, it was agreed that James would meet up with us and we would measure the height of a mountain. We could then see for ourselves whether the technique was capable of doing what we wanted. So, it came to pass that a team comprising John Barnard, Graham Jackson and Myrddyn Phillips, and John & Anne Nuttall, (who had introduced Myrddyn to us), set out with David Purchase, Dewi Jones, Harold Morris and James Whitworth to measure the heights of Craig Fach (in the Snowdon Group) and Mynydd Graig Goch (above Nantlle). While the former fell well short of the magic number, Mynydd Graig Goch came in at 609.75m or 2,000.5ft. This height was confirmed by Ordnance Survey with whom James worked closely. So, Wales had its new 2,000ft mountain! More importantly we learned that the technology was easily capable of determining heights to 5cm, or even less, if sufficient data were collected and if the data were processed in leading edge software.

It was this that brought us to that meeting place with the world's media and later in the day a press conference at Plas Tan y Bwlch, the Snowdonia National Park Environmental Studies Centre. After our presentation, we were approached by Fred Ward, who introduced himself as Treasurer of The Munro Society (TMS). Fred explained the exciting project of 'Heighting' (as the process became known) all the mountains in Scotland that were close to the Munro – Corbett boundary. The feasibility study with CMCR Ltd had been successful, but now the Society was wishing to continue the work and was seeking expertise to do so. Accordingly, Fred asked if we were interested. The answer was 'Yes, once we have purchased our gear!' Several meetings with James Whitworth resulted in our purchase of a Leica 530 GPS receiver and our bank balances becoming several thousand pounds lighter. Calling ourselves G&J Surveys made us feel better about it! It was then that we arranged to meet up with Fred Ward and Iain Robertson at a hotel meeting room in Kendal to discuss the project. Despite playing a major role in the press conference and also having accompanied us on some of our line surveys in Wales, Myrddyn declined our invitation to attend the meeting because his interests lay in the mountains of Wales. So it was that we met up with Fred Ward and Iain Robertson. We learnt all about the project and were enthusiastic to take part. We explained how we would carry out the work and in return The Munro Society would cover the expenses for the two of us and contribute towards the maintenance of the equipment. We had a deal to measure two mountains subject to agreement by the TMS Executive, agreement that was subsequently given. Those two mountains were to be Beinn Teallach and Ben Vane and these surveys were scheduled for 15th and 16th May 2009. As the time approached and our enthusiasm grew, Myrddyn was invited to join the Heightings Project as a guest of The Munro Society. So, on 14th May 2009 we travelled north with him to begin what proved to be an exciting chapter, both for us and for TMS!

In this chapter we describe the basics of the techniques we used in the project and how they were applied in the surveys.

Surveying and Geomatics

Definition

Surveying has historically been defined as the science of determining the relative positions of points on or beneath the Earth's surface or of establishing such points. However, now the definition is more general, since it is regarded as the discipline which includes every method for measuring and collecting information about the physical Earth and our environment. It also includes the processing of the information and its publishing for a wide range of usage. Surveying certainly is not new and its first use was probably in 1400BC when Herodotus recorded that Sesotris divided Egypt up into a range of plots for the purposes of taxation. Surveyors were employed to continually re-establish boundaries that were washed away in the Nile floods. Certainly, there are many examples throughout history where surveying was used to establish boundaries for land 'ownership'. However, there has always been a growing demand for maps or diagrams showing spatial arrangements. This is well described for the UK in Rachel Hewitt's book 'Map of a Nation' which is essentially a Biography of Ordnance Survey with military use being the key initial driver.

There is now globally a wide range of professional bodies that promote and encourage all aspects of surveying to meet more and more challenging problems. In English-speaking nations, the new term Geomatics is used instead of surveying and the word is used to describe the areas of practice. The name change has arisen because of the way that surveying practice has changed recently through technological developments. Traditionally a surveyor would have made ground-based measurements with transits, early theodolites, to measure angles and tapes or chains to measure distances. Then, through complex and tediously time-consuming calculations, the data would have to be processed manually to present a map or diagram in hard copy. However, geomatics is now a global science and the modern surveyor uses electronic instruments for measuring angles and distances as well as instruments using satellite systems, computers, graphic systems etc., with all the 'bells and whistles' to accompany them. The surveyor's life today has been made much easier to obtain good and accurate data and present it, but the science behind geomatics is exceedingly complex and an "industry" in itself.

Triangulation

One of the fundamental mathematical principles underlying surveying is that of triangulation which is encompassed in the branch of mathematics called trigonometry. One supposes it depends on your age and what school you went to, but the authors remember using triangulation concepts to measure the heights of buildings or trees and widths of rivers, a great excuse to get out of the classroom! So how does triangulation work and why is it so important?

Consider the simple triangle ABC shown below. The lengths of the sides of the triangle are denoted by a, b and c and the angles by A, B and C. These are related by the mathematical formula called the Sine Rule:

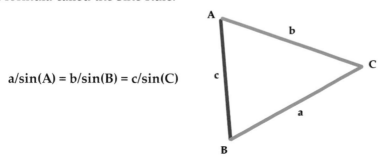

$$a/sin(A) = b/sin(B) = c/sin(C)$$

If the angles A and B are known, then using the fact that all the three internal angles of a triangle add up to 180 degrees, angle C is easily calculated. Now sin(A), sin(B) and sin(C) are found through standard functions on calculators, computers, or in tables, and if distance c is known, then distances a and b can be calculated from the Sine Rule. The relevance to surveying can now be seen since points A and B could, for example, be triangulation pillars whose positions and heights are known. We need to find the position and height of point C. The angles A and B in both the vertical and horizontal planes can be measured with a theodolite and distance c is known from the triangulation network data, therefore the position and height of point C can be calculated.

The principle described above in the three dimensions; Latitude, Longitude and Height, was used by Ordnance Survey to map the UK. A three-dimensional interlocking network of triangles was created across the whole country, OSGB36, as exemplified by the system of trig pillars, which then allowed any point to be surveyed using the process of triangulation. Even though surveyors now generally use satellite technology to replace optical measurements with theodolites, the principles of triangulation are still the basics of the mathematics to find positions and heights. The same applies to photogrammetry, mapping with aerial photography, which is now used by Ordnance Survey for the regular mapping of the UK.

Dealing with Measurement Errors

When taking any scientific measurement the possibility of errors must be taken into account and an estimate of the total error on the final measurement is made. Without this, one would have no idea actually how good the measurement is. There are three types of error that can occur:- Systematic Errors, Random Errors and 'Gross' errors.

By 'Gross' errors we mean mistakes made by the operators. It is possible to misread the staff measurement or not enter the correct height in the processing software of the GNSS (Global Navigation Satellite System) receiver above the measurement point and mistakes like these could cause sizeable errors in the final result. However, by careful double checking throughout all the processes we use to obtain a measurement, we believe that we have taken steps to eliminate this type of error. It usually occurs through inadequate working practices and we believe we have eliminated those from our survey technique.

Systematic Errors are errors associated with the equipment. Often there is little that can be done about these, but being aware of the possibilities allows one to reduce them by careful design of the measurement. Systematic errors associated with GNSS receivers are small since much thought has gone into their design by the manufacturers to eliminate these possibilities. Perhaps the most significant systematic error in the equipment we use for surveys is a misalignment of the optics within the automatic level. However, we regularly check this and, although minimised, it is also possible to eliminate this in the way measurements are made. Single optical measurements made over long distances are prone to this error. This was not the case for the surveys carried out in this project.

Finally, we are left with random errors in the measurements. Although all attempts can be made to eliminate these it is not possible to do so and therefore their overall effect on the final measurement needs to be estimated. Random errors and individual steps taken to reduce them or measure them are described in other sections but how are these combined to give a final estimate of accuracy?

The overall estimate of error **E** is given by the equation:

$$\mathbf{E} = +/- \sqrt{(E_1^2 + E_2^2 + E_3^2 + \ldots)}$$

Where E_1, E_2, E_3 … are estimates of individual errors contributing to the final error, assuming these to be independent of one another.

As an example, assume we are measuring the height of a hill. We can estimate that the summit position had been located by automatic level and staff to an accuracy of +/-0.02m and that the height error for a two-hour GNSS dataset was +/-0.08m. Using the above formula, the overall error is:

$$E = +/- \sqrt{(0.02^2 + 0.08^2)} = +/-0.082m$$

Since the individual errors were estimates then we would probably quote the overall height measurement to the nearest centimetre and say that the overall error was +/-0.08m. In this example it is clear that the height error in the location of the summit position is not significant in the overall error.

Earth Curvature

A factor that makes the measurement of height more complex is that we live on the surface of a spheroid. If you stand at a point on the Earth looking horizontally from that point at some distant feature, for example the top of a hill, the hill will appear lower than it really is. This is because the curvature of the Earth causes the ground to 'drop away' from a horizontal line. For short distances the curvature of the Earth has little effect on topological height and for 1,000m distance the effect is 8cm. However, this effect is not linear with distance and for a distance of 2,500m, Earth curvature results in a height 'drop' of 0.5m and clearly needs to be taken into account in any measurement system. A chart showing the effect of Earth curvature on vertical height is shown below.

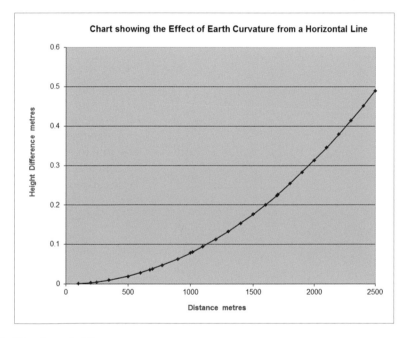

What is Horizontal?

Gravity, the force towards the 'centre of the Earth', that keeps us on the Earth's surface is the force that enables us to define horizontal as the perpendicular plane to vertical. As we live on the surface of a spheroid, vertical and therefore horizontal, will depend on our position and will vary in a complex way. In a simple model, we can consider the earth as a uniform sphere where the direction of gravity is always to the centre of the sphere. As we move across the Earth's surface the horizontal is always perpendicular to the line to the centre of the sphere and therefore varies in a regular manner. However, the Earth's shape is not a sphere but more of an ellipsoid as though the spherical shape had been squeezed at the poles which caused a bulge at the equator. Assuming the Earth still to have a uniform density, the force of gravity will always be to the centre of the Earth's mass. The horizontal at any point will still be a plane perpendicular to the vertical but it will not vary in a consistent manner as for the spherical model. Unfortunately, although better than a sphere, the ellipsoidal shape of the Earth is still an approximation. There are bulges and depressions on the land mass of the Earth's crust and these can happen even on a very local scale. These irregularities, on and under the Earth's surface, cause local concentrations and variations in the Earth's density, which distort the direction of the force of gravity and hence the direction of the horizontal plane. Most of the time we would not be able to detect these distortions, unless specialist instruments are used. (The science for making these measurements is called gravimetry.) However, these distortions have a very important effect on topological surveying since they define the shape of the Geoid model (see separate section) which determines the reference from which heights are measured.

Ordnance Datum Newlyn – ODN

Whenever a physical measurement is made it has to be made to some reference. We have international standards for physical constants, for example kilograms and metres, and all measurements are made relative to those standards. However, when topological height is defined, not only do we need the units of measurement, that is metres or feet, but we need to relate it to some base. Ben Nevis is quoted as having a height of 1,345m but what is the frame of reference? Often one hears people say "that is height above sea level", MSL (mean sea level), which of course then leads to the debate whether the heights of hills and mountains are changing because of rising sea levels due to global warming! Of course, MSL is changing with time but it also varies around the coastline of the UK depending where the measurement is taken. So this means that MSL cannot be defined accurately enough to be used as a standard for topographical height.

The reference adopted by Ordnance Survey for mainland Great Britain is Ordnance Datum Newlyn (ODN). This is the average sea level measured by the tide gauge at Newlyn in Cornwall between 1915 and 1921 and is the adopted zero height. Previous to Newlyn the MSL datum for GB was measured at Liverpool but Newlyn was chosen for its more open exposure to the Atlantic which should result in a more accurate estimation of MSL. Because of rising sea level, the MSL at Newlyn no longer corresponds with ODN. However, that does not matter since the difference is not too great, under 1 metre. If a decision were made that ODN is no longer applicable as a standard, then the consequences to national mapping would be quite serious. Basically, all contours and heights would need to be changed on every map – a mammoth and quite pointless task! The tide gauge at Newlyn still exists, but more practically there is an Ordnance Survey benchmark that directly relates to ODN and therefore can be used as the reference point for practical measurements. This is a bolt positioned in the floor of the tidal observatory and is below a protective cover so cannot be seen by the general public. It is 4.571m higher than ODN.

It should be noted that the Scottish Islands, Scilly and the Isle of Man have different MSL datums.

The Global Reference for Surveying – WGS84

As stated in the previous section the GB reference from which heights are measured is ODN. However, other countries chose their own reference points for zero height and this has resulted in numerous different height standards that have been adopted that are suitable to the particular country's needs. Normally if you buy a modern map abroad, the practical zero height reference model will be stated. So if you take your hand-held Garmin GNSS receiver abroad then in the 'settings' menu you should be able to select the appropriate reference that will relate your measurements to directly what is stated on the map.

Modern use for satellites, including surveying, has required a global reference system to define the Earth's 'surface' and position on it. As individual satellites orbit the Earth, their positions relative to the earth need to be known accurately, if they are to be used for surveying and navigation. This requires that the global reference system has to be fixed in a position relative to the Earth to provide a Coordinate System known as Latitude, Longitude and Ellipsoidal Height or alternatively in a Cartesian Coordinate system of X, Y and Z. The currently adopted system is known as WGS84 (World Geodetic System 1984). WGS84 is essentially a best fit ellipsoid to the shape of the Earth. It is derived from previous ellipsoid models of the Earth based on the assumption that it would try to best represent global ocean levels, assuming all the oceans were joined, free from the effects of tides, ocean currents and weather. When we consider the surface of a lake we would say it was 'level'. In more scientific terms, the potential energy, the energy due to height, is consistent across the whole surface. This is also true for the WGS84 ellipsoid.

Since 1984, the WGS84 system has undergone a couple of revisions to improve its accuracy and the coordinate system related to it is now the default system for Global Navigation Satellite System (GNSS) receivers. Not only does this apply to specialist receivers such as the Leica Viva GS15 we use, but to all hand-held GPS units and SatNavs. So when one of these receivers measures height, its default measurement is the height above the WGS84 ellipsoid model and is known as the ellipsoidal height.

Geoid Models in GB – OSGM02 and OSGM15

So far we have discussed measurements of height made from MSL at Newlyn in Cornwall as the reference and also from the global system WGS84. However, these heights will not be the same. The main reason for this is that although WGS84 is designed as the best global fit for 'sea level' it is not particularly good for the reference zero height for the UK. In fact the height of WGS84 across the UK is about 50m lower than ODN derived heights. So in WGS84 the height of Ben Nevis would be about 1,400m instead of 1,345m as we now know it to be!

The difference is resolved with the use of a local Geoid model. When a height is measured it can be done by levelling with theodolites and levels from ODN to the point to be measured. However, heights are now measured with GNSS receivers which give the height above the WGS84 ellipsoid. Therefore, a model of the varying height offset between WGS84 and Newlyn is needed underneath the land mass of the UK and this is the Geoid model. The Ordnance Survey's current geoid model is known as OSGM15 since it was established in 2015. For the work carried out in this project the previous model OSGM02 (released in 2002) was used. In general, the revision of OSGM02 to OSGM15 only caused a centimetre or two difference to measured heights and as heights on OS maps are rounded to the nearest metre, the revision made almost no difference to map heights. However, in certain areas of Scotland, notably the Western Isles, some heights changed by up to 0.5m. We have checked the heights of hills measured in this project and although the change from OSGM02 to OSGM15 caused measured heights to change by a few centimetres, no hill classifications were altered by this change.

So when we measure a height in the UK using a GNSS receiver a transformation is applied to ellipsoid height, relating to WGS84, to give the MSL height, the height relating to ODN. The mathematical equation to do this is very simple:

$$h = H - N$$

where H is the ellipsoidal height relating to WGS84, N is the height difference between the MSL surface and the WGS84 surface and h is then defined as the orthometric height. As already stated, in the UK WGS84 lies below ODN, by about 50m. Therefore, N is positive and is known as the Geoid-ellipsoid separation. The Geoid is a complex surface so N varies with position. The OSGM models mapping the changes in N and therefore orthometric heights, heights based on ODN, can be measured anywhere in the UK using GNSS technology plus the OSGM model.

The Global Navigation Satellite System (GNSS)

Introduction

We have already described the traditional methods of surveying which were carried out until near the end of the last century and where the OSGB36 Terrestrial Reference Frame was realised using a network of triangulation pillars. These have now been replaced by GNSS technology, familiarly known as GPS (Global Positioning System) which more properly describes the first available system provided by a network of American satellites. We will briefly mention other systems later in the chapter. The principle of the system is simple, but it is its implementation that is more complicated.

GPS simply measures the distance between a fixed point (your position) and several satellites in the sky. If the position of the satellites is known and their respective distances from you are known at that instant, then your position relative to them can be calculated. Note that as long as you are within the sphere contained by the satellites orbits, then your position can be calculated anywhere within that, you do not have to be on the surface of the Earth. In principle determining your position can be achieved by measuring your distance from three satellites. This will give a position of the most basic quality so in practice four or more measurements are taken since this allows for a more robust position computation.

The signal transmitted by a satellite is encoded with a time signal generated by the satellite's on-board atomic clock. This signal is an electromagnetic wave and therefore like any electromagnetic wave, for example a radio signal, it travels at the speed of light. The time that the signal is received by the GPS receiver is recorded by its clock which is accurate, but not as accurate as an atomic clock. The time difference multiplied by the speed of light gives the approximate distance between the receiver and the satellite. This approximate distance is termed a pseudorange.

$$\text{Pseudorange} = \text{time difference} \ \times \ \text{speed of light}$$

It is termed a pseudorange because it contains errors such as in the time measurement from the receiver's clock and the atomic clock on the satellite will also contain a tiny error. Other errors in the signal travel time will be introduced by the different layers of the atmosphere that it has to travel through. To obtain the true distance or range between receiver and satellite these errors have to be determined and removed. Taking pseudoranges from at least four satellites enables the mathematics required to compute the receiver clock error but without further processing the other errors remain in the pseudorange.

So far, we have assumed that the position of a satellite is known. Each satellite transmits a signal that is encoded with its orbit parameters or elements; this is termed the Navigation Message. It enables the receiver to compute the satellites position in the sky in much the same way as an astronomer can compute the orbit of a moon, planet or comet around its parent body. Thus, the position of any satellite can be computed by the receiver at any moment in time from the Navigation Message.

GNSS Elements

Any GNSS system is made up of three elements which are:

1. A constellation of satellites that send positional information to the user

2. A control centre that monitors and communicates with the satellites. The control centre maintains the orbits of the satellites and will bring satellites into or out of service as required.

3. A network of Ground Tracking Centres that provide information for the published ephemerides that are employed by users to predict where the satellites are in the sky at any moment in time.

All of these three elements are vital to the correct operation of the system for the end user whose receiver hardware and processing software rely on it.

The element we 'see' as end users is the constellation of satellites. For the American GPS constellation, these satellites, of which there are 24 (more recently the number of satellites in the constellation has been increased) in operation at any one time, are set in orbits that are about 20,000km above the Earth's surface and they are travelling at about 4km/s relative to the centre of the Earth and in a direction that is the same as the Earth's rotation. A satellite weighs about 2,000kg, is about 5m long and has a lifetime of about eight years. It carries rubidium and caesium atomic clocks powered by solar panels. The orbit of each satellite is elliptical, but very nearly circular, with the centre of the Earth at one focus. There are six equally spaced orbits altogether, each containing four satellites set approximately, but not necessarily exactly, at 90 degrees to one another in any one orbit. The orbital planes are set to the Earth's equator at an angle of 55 degrees and, since there are six orbits that are equally distributed around the Earth, they are at 60 degrees to one another. The satellites obey Kepler's Law, as do all astronomical bodies (to a first approximation), and so by knowing the six parameters that define an orbit and time it is possible to predict the position of the satellite in the sky at any instant.

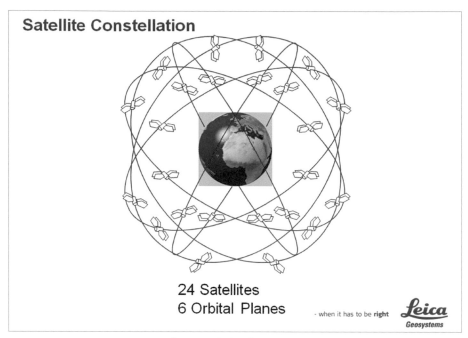

Courtesy Leica Geosystems

The geometry of the orbits leads to an orbital period of just under 12hr, in fact it is 11hr 58min which means two orbits are completed in 23hr 56min and this coincides with one complete rotation of the Earth (the sidereal day). Consequently, the same satellite is over the same location on the Earth once every 23hr 56min, that is, the satellite constellation geometry repeats every sidereal day.

For a user in Britain, the consequence of orbits with a 55 degree inclination to the equator means that there are few or no satellites in the northern sky, depending upon one's exact latitude, and those in the north-eastern and north-western sky will tend to be near the horizon. Therefore, in hilly or urban terrains where large sections of the sky may be hidden, it is important to site a receiver, if possible, with a good view of the southern sky. If only the northern sky is visible, due to hilly terrain or buildings blocking the southern sky, then height positioning may be slightly poorer in these circumstances. A similar situation arises if most satellites happen to be near the horizon, which is unusual in Britain but commonplace in extreme northern latitudes. These situations are also prone to multipath, a term that describes a situation where satellite signals are reflected from nearby objects. This phenomenon results in poorer determinations of position and height.

Measurement of Time Difference

The time taken for a signal from the satellite to reach the GNSS receiver is very short. The satellite is on average about 20,000km above the Earth and the speed of light is 3×10^8 ms^{-1} so this time is approximately $(2 \times 10^7)/(3 \times 10^8) = 0.07$sec. The atomic clock on the satellite does not send out a series of time pips like a speaking clock! The method is much more elegant than this.

There are two carrier signals generated from the on-board atomic clock, an L1 channel (wavelength 19.0cm) and an L2 channel (wavelength 24.4cm) and information is encoded on to these. L1 carries a coarse acquisition code which is used by the receiver for locking on initially to the satellite. It repeats every 1millisecond. The coarse acquisition code is also unique to each satellite, thus enabling the receiver to identify that satellite. This channel also carries the Navigation Message which encompasses information on the satellite orbital parameters, almanac data, satellite clock corrections and ionosphere information. L1 and L2 both carry a precise (so called 'P') code that is identical to each channel and has a much longer repeat of 267 days and thereby a higher resolution than the Coarse Acquisition code. It is used by the receiver for precise measurement of location but is only available to authorised (mainly military) users.

The GNSS receiver also generates its own electronic replica of the satellite's signals which is synchronised with its own clock. The receiver then compares its own replica signal with the incoming signal from the satellite and matches the two. Clearly there will be a displacement of the two signals in time since it takes about 0.07sec for the signal to travel from the satellite to the receiver. On top of this the time errors in the receiver clock and the satellite clock will also be incorporated into the displacement. It is this displacement in the two signals that the receiver is actually measuring.

For the pseudorange from one satellite we know the position (x_s, y_s, z_s) in polar coordinates) of the satellite and the clock error for the atomic clock on the satellite which is given in the Navigation Message. We do not know the polar coordinates x_r, y_r, z_r of the receiver (that is our position on the Earth) or the clock error of the receiver. So for one satellite we may use Pythagoras' Theorem to construct an equation for the range, that is, the distance between the satellite and the receiver:

$$R = ((x_s - x_r)^2 + (y_s - y_r)^2 + (z_s - z_r)^2)^{1/2} + c\tau_r - c\tau_s$$

where

      R is the range
      x_s is the x coordinate of the satellite at transmit time
      y_s is the y coordinate of the satellite at transmit time
      z_s is the z coordinate of the satellite at transmit time
      x_r is the x coordinate of the receiver at receive time
      y_r is the y coordinate of the receiver at receive time
      z_r is the z coordinate of the receiver at receive time
      τ_r is the clock error of the receiver
      τ_s is the clock error of the satellite
      c is the speed of light

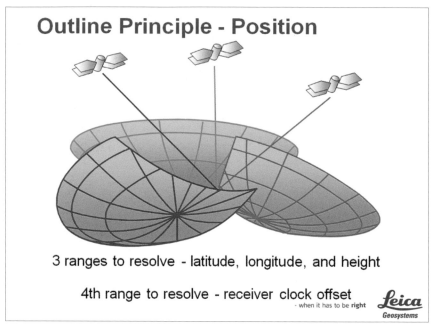

Courtesy Leica Geosystems

So we have an equation with four unknowns. In order to find our position, therefore, we require similar information from at least three more satellites in order to solve for the four unknowns and determine our position. Data from more satellites will give a more precise solution. These data from all n satellites that are within view of the receiver are assembled into a matrix and x_r, y_r, and z_r and the receiver clock error are determined by a least squares solution.

A More Accurate Solution

What has been described so far works well for determining position, but there is an alternative method available to surveyors, which is used for higher precision applications. Instead of directly measuring the time taken for a satellite signal to reach the receiver, the surveyor uses the phase of the received signal. The receiver takes the satellite signal and multiplies this with its own replica signal to produce a beat signal. While it is a simplification, it may be thought that the receiver then counts the number of complete oscillations plus the phase of the incomplete cycle of the beat signal. The wavelength of the beat signal is known and therefore the distance between the satellite and the receiver may be calculated.

If the receiver is close to trees, buildings, or natural features such as crags or cliffs, then these features may reflect the satellite signals into the receiver. This results in the receiver losing count of the number of complete cycles, a situation known as cycle slip. Much research has been carried out to develop algorithms that tackle this issue and resolve it.

Corrections – General

The above description is GNSS technology in its simplest terms, but for higher precision several corrections have to be applied. The largest is the receiver clock error which if not computed, as described above, could give positional errors of a few hundred metres.

The Ionospheric Correction

The largest correction, after the receiver clock error, is the ionospheric correction. The higher levels of the atmosphere are bombarded by the solar wind, and molecules there absorb this energy and lose electrons, themselves becoming positively charged in the process. Electromagnetic waves (the signals from the satellites) interact with these charged particles and are slowed down as a result, the magnitude of the effect being dependent on the electron density of the ionosphere. Consequently, this retardation is manifested as an error in receiver position. The size of the error is dependent on solar activity, whether surveying is taking place during night time or daytime and, very significantly, the position of the satellite with respect to the receiver. For a satellite near the horizon the signal passes for a greater distance through the ionosphere to the receiver, so the retardation is greater than for a satellite near the zenith. Typically, the retardation leads to an error of between 5m and 10m in the determination of position, but the error can be several tens of metres for satellites near the horizon. This is one reason why receivers are often set up with a 15 degree cut off angle, that is, they do not collect data from satellites that are less than 15 degrees to the horizon. Survey-grade GNSS receivers are capable of receiving Precise Acquisition code both from the L1 and L2 channels of the satellite, and these channels operate at different wavelengths as described in the previous section. Higher frequencies (e.g. the L1 signal) are retarded by the ionosphere less than lower frequencies (the L2 signal) and this effect is well understood and can be modelled accurately. Consequently, the effect of ionospheric retardation can be largely eliminated during processing in proprietary software.

The Tropospheric Correction

Retardation of the satellite signals by the troposphere is less than for the ionosphere and typically leads to corrections of about 1m in position. It is caused by refraction and leads to an increased path length and therefore an apparent increase in the measured distance between receiver and satellite. It is independent of wavelength and comprises two components, retardation by dry air and retardation by water vapour. The dry air component is relatively easy to model and is directly related to the density of the air which in turn is determined by air pressure and temperature. It comprises about 90% of the retardation. This is fortunate because the distribution of water vapour in the troposphere is very variable and therefore the effect of water vapour is very difficult to model.

There are several models that have been developed to determine the tropospheric correction and these are usually incorporated into commercially available processing software. For example, Leica GeoOffice (GPS data processing software) offers Hopfield, Saastamoinen and Essen & Froome models as well as a Computed option. This last model takes a fraction of the collected experimental data and determines the correction from that. All models are most successful when applied to situations where the satellites are high in the sky and therefore the path length of the signals through the atmosphere is shorter. They work less well for satellites near the horizon where the path length through the atmosphere is long, another reason why receivers are often set with a cut off angle of 15 degrees.

Other Corrections

There are other, generally smaller, errors that occur which also must be corrected. One of these is the satellite clock error, a large proportion of which is due to relativity. The satellites are situated about 20,000km above the Earth and therefore the atomic clocks on board the satellites experience a lower gravity than a similar clock on Earth. In accordance with Einstein's General Theory of Relativity this causes them to run about 45 microseconds a day faster than an equivalent clock on earth. At the same time the satellites are travelling at about 4km/sec which in accordance with Einstein's Special Theory of Relativity causes the satellites' clocks to run about 7 microseconds a day slower than an equivalent clock on Earth. The net effect is that the satellites' clocks appear to be running 38 microseconds a day faster than an equivalent clock on Earth. This error is corrected and broadcast in the Navigation message.

Another minor error occurs that is related to the Broadcast Ephemeris for each satellite. The Broadcast Ephemeris is the predicted position of the satellite at any moment in the future and is calculated from tracking data supplied by the monitoring stations. It forms part of the Navigation Message. A Precise Ephemeris is published about a week in arrears and this is derived from the actual tracking data recorded by the monitoring stations for the time period of interest. The error in using Broadcast Ephemeris data can be of the order of a metre in position for a stand-alone solution, that is, where position is calculated solely from the data acquired by a single receiver (see later).

Lastly, there is receiver noise caused by thermal or dynamic stress in the receiver itself. It is a very small effect, of the order of a few centimetres, and for most purposes may be ignored.

Accuracy

Despite the complexity of the system and the number of corrections that need to be made, the accuracy of GNSS is remarkably good. For any receiver the measurement error for height is always greater than for position. For example, hand-held Garmin receivers have a positional error of about 7m-8m or less, whereas that for height is in the range 10m – 15m. From our own experience, the error in position for raw data from our Leica 530 and Leica Viva GS15 receivers, with which heightings for The Munro Society were conducted, is about 1 – 2m for position and usually 5m or less for height. On rare occasions we have seen height errors of 10m. On that basis then, how can we claim measurement errors of +/-0.05m, which we do in many of our reports?

Differential GNSS

So far we have been considering the situation where there is a single stand-alone receiver collecting data from several satellites (usually six or more) in order to calculate its position and the above measurement uncertainties relate to this geometry. However, there is another geometry in which the receiver relates its position to one or more other receivers and this technique is termed Differential GNSS. In its simplest form a surveyor may set up one GNSS receiver as a base station collecting satellite data and then use another receiver to collect satellite data at another position. Provided the two receivers are relatively close (usually less than 100km), then many of the errors will be the same for both receivers and a combined calculation using data from both receivers will produce a very accurate position and height difference between the two receivers. This idea can be taken one stage further.

In the UK there is a network (known as 'OS Net') of approximately 110 base stations owned and operated by Ordnance Survey and these are spread evenly over the country with an average separation of about 70km. These base stations comprise a highly accurate GNSS receiver and very rigidly mounted antenna. These base stations are continuously recording data from GNSS satellites with the data stored by a central control facility. The positions of the base stations are now known very accurately indeed with respect to one another – 2mm horizontally and 6mm vertically. Moreover, the whole network has been related to the Terrestial Reference Frame OSGB36 (see Triangulation) through the National Grid transformation OSTN15 so the Cartesian coordinates calculated from GNSS may be easily transformed to National Grid coordinates. There are two ways to access the network.

The first is by a method termed Real Time Kinematic (RTK). In this method the user's receiver is linked to the control system of the network by a mobile phone link, so that data from the nearest base stations (those nearer than about 100km) can be fed directly to the receiver's controller along with the receiver's data. This allows processing of the receiver's position and height to be carried out in real time. The great advantage of this method is that it gives an immediate result while the surveyor is on site. The downside is that it requires a mobile phone link and mobile phone signals are not always available. Consequently, many users of RTK buy SIM cards from several mobile phone providers which is expensive and, moreover, mobile phone signals are often not available in the mountain environment anyway. RTK itself is also expensive with a licence from the instrument manufacturer costing between £1,500 and £2,000 per annum. For these reasons we have chosen the second option.

This second option accesses the base station data via the Ordnance Survey website. Data become available usually no more than one hour after collection and may be downloaded to a computer free of charge. The user's survey position is given along with the time window required and the number of base stations required (based on either number or distance). The downloaded file may then be processed along with the user's data file in suitable software.

Differential GNSS that makes use of the Ordnance Survey base station network yields results that are about two orders of magnitude more accurate than stand-alone solutions. Typically, the second method described above yields, for two hours of data collection, a positional accuracy of about 0.01m and height accuracy of about 0.05m (to three standard deviations) when a survey grade receiver, such as the Leica Viva GS15, is used. RTK is nearly as good. It should be added that base stations situated 100km away or less from the user's position are employed in this post processing exercise, because tropospheric conditions are usually fairly consistent over this range. Hence errors due to changing atmospheric conditions are minimised.

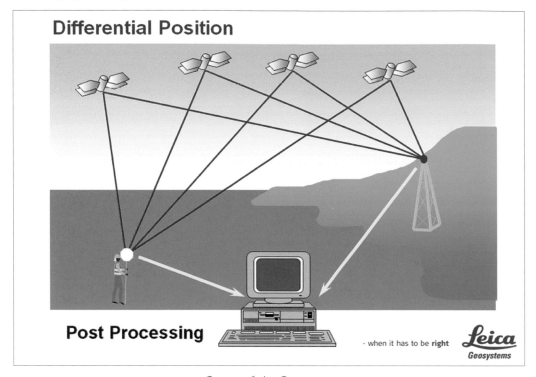

Differential Position

Post Processing

- when it has to be right **Leica**
Geosystems

Courtesy Leica Geosystems

Dilution of Precision

The computation of the user's position from all the satellite data contains information on the measurement uncertainty associated with that solution. The two most used terms are Vertical Dilution of Precision (VDOP) and Horizontal Dilution of Precision (HDOP). For example, a calculated VDOP of 5 means that pseudorange errors of, say, 1m will lead to vertical position errors of 5m. DOP values are produced and may be displayed during data collection on our Leica instruments and enable the user to determine the quality of the data being collected and whether to continue or abort the survey at that time.

Mission Planning

DOP values can also be used in forward planning. Commercial software takes the satellite almanac, which is available in the Navigation Message from the satellite, and from this plots the positions of satellites for future times for the geographical location of interest. From these positions DOP values are calculated and from these the quality of GNSS data is predicted. This enables the user to determine the best time window in which to collect data. We have used this technique on several occasions to give us confidence that the time window in which we envisage collecting data for Munro Society surveys have favourable satellite geometries.

Shown below is a typical satellite almanac predicting the availability of GPS satellites at a specific location about two weeks in the future over a 24 hour period. Although this type of almanac is available on the internet, it is broadcast by the satellite system and collected as a dataset on a GNSS receiver. The software used to process GNSS data can usually display the almanac output in a readily usable form, in this case to users of Leica GeoOffice software. The background colour shows the number of satellites available at a particular time as shown by the scale on the vertical right-hand axis. Also plotted on this almanac are the VDOP measurements, although a range of other options is also possible, and its scale is shown on the left-hand vertical axis. The VDOP value at any time is displayed by the black line.

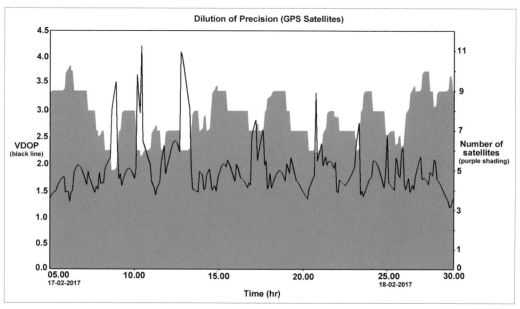

Courtesy Leica GeoOffice

The almanac plot shows its value in mission planning, as it allows periods when there is poor satellite coverage to be avoided in the survey. The plot shows the range of satellites that are available is between 5 and 11. Ideally for surveys with a Leica SR530 GNSS receiver experience has shown receiving data from 7 or more satellites at any particular time is satisfactory for a good result. Therefore, in the planned survey one would try to avoid, if possible, those periods where only 5 or 6 satellites were available. (We have seen some almanacs showing as few as 4 satellites being available but this is not common now). If not possible then one would have the knowledge to use a longer collection time to compensate. The effect of reduced satellite availability is reflected in the VDOP values. The line showing the VDOP value for most of the 24 hour period is between 1.5 and 2. However, when satellite availability drops to 5 satellites, the VDOP value increases to about 4. So here is a measure that tells the surveyor that the error in the factors affecting the precision of the measurement have worsened by a factor of approximately two.

Further Developments in GNSS Technology

In recent years other countries have begun to develop their own GNSS technology. Besides GPS, the system developed by the United States, the only other fully operational system is that developed by Russia and called the GLObal NAvigation Satellite System (GLONASS). This system has twenty four operational satellites in three orbital planes. From the UK up to nine satellites are visible at any one time and these may be used along with the American GPS satellites by the latest generation receivers, like our own Leica Viva GS15. The ability to detect and use these extra satellites improves accuracy in situations where there is a limited view of the sky, or where reflections from cliffs or buildings can interfere with reception.

One of the advantages of being able to use the GLONASS satellites, in addition to the GPS system arises from the improved overall availability of GNSS data. Shown below is a satellite almanac over the same time period as shown in the previous section, but it now includes the GLONASS satellites. The range of satellites available to provide GNSS data is now between 10 and 18. The VDOP values have also improved by approximately a factor of two. For most of the 24 hour period they lie between 1.0 and 1.4 (cf 1.5 and 2.0 without GLONASS) but only reach a maximum value of 2.2 (cf 4.1 without GLONASS).

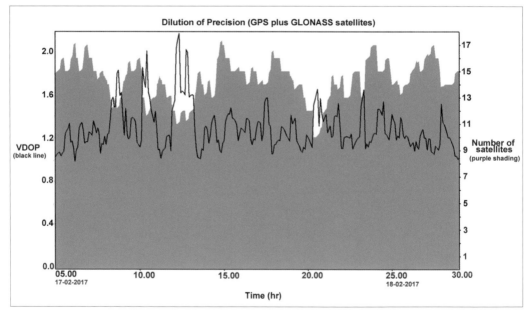

Courtesy Leica GeoOffice

Although the presence of GLONASS satellites predicts an improvement in precision as shown by the decrease in VDOP, for long static surveys their effect on precision is not that marked. The major benefit of GLONASS, in addition to GPS satellites, arises when GNSS data collection times are short or, due to the geography of the survey point, satellite reception is limited due to obstructions. In these cases the GLONASS satellites can sometimes make all the difference between an unacceptable survey and an acceptable one.

Europe is developing its own GNSS global network called Galileo. The plan is to have a fully operational system in place by 2020. As of December 2016 the system has 18 of 30 satellites in orbit. Galileo started offering Early Operational Capability (EOC) on 15th December 2016 and is expected to reach Full Operational Capability (FOC) in 2019.

China has developed a regional Satellite Navigation System called BeiDou. Although at the moment this is only a regional system for South East Asia, it is planned to be a global network by 2020.

Similarly, Japan's Quasi Zenith Satellite System (QZSS) and India's Regional Navigation Satellite System (IRNSS) are regional systems only at the moment, but no firm plans have been announced for expanding these into global networks.

In addition there are satellite-based augmentation systems (SBAS). As the term suggests these are not navigations systems in their own right, but instead they augment currently operating systems, such as GPS by improving their accuracy and reliability through the correction of signal measurement errors. There are several systems available around the world, two being the Wide-Area Augmentation System (WAAS) operated in the United States and the European Geo Stationary Navigation Overlay Service (EGNOS). Most hand-held GNSS receivers can receive and utilise the satellite signals from the WAAS systems. Normally this needs to be switched on in the receiver's setup menu and in Garmin instruments the letter "d" will appear on a bar in the satellite screen if WAAS corrections are being made to that particular satellite signal.

Chapter 6

The Surveys in Practice

John Barnard and Graham Jackson

Specification

Standard Requirements of The Munro Society

The Scottish Mountaineering Club accepts proposed changes to the lists it publishes in *Munro's Tables* and its guide books provided these have been ratified by Ordnance Survey. This ensures that changes have been properly vetted by the United Kingdom's Mapping Agency and carried out to its standards. Consequently, a key element of our surveys for TMS was that our surveys would be submitted to Ordnance Survey for verification. Accordingly, Ordnance Survey set out a number of conditions that we should follow for its verification of our proposed surveys. The key ones from a practical standpoint were:

1. *We would locate the summit with a surveyor's level and staff.* The use of this equipment allows summits to be located to within 1cm of height for the mountains of interest for this project. For lower hills where summits may be covered in coarse vegetation or peat hags the measurement uncertainty is slightly greater, but this does not generally apply to the higher mountains in the UK. A rotating laser unit and staff performs a similar purpose, but is more expensive and heavier, while other methods such as hand levels and laser tape measures have poorer precision and accuracy, especially over distances greater than 5m or so. So condition one was that we use a surveyor's level and staff.

2. *Once the GNSS receiver had locked on to satellites, we would collect 2hr or more of data.* From the above discussion on GNSS technology it is clear that there are several potential sources of error that require minimisation and 2hr of data allows this to be done under most circumstances. For example, the software uses a proportion of the data for determining the tropospheric error, as already described. It does not mean that acceptable results cannot be achieved with a smaller dataset; it does mean that the measurement uncertainty is greater and if a map is going to be changed as a result of a survey then, not unreasonably, OS wanted the dataset to be as robust as possible.

3. *The height of the antenna above the ground should be measured and recorded for error checking purposes.*

4. *The antenna must be securely supported on a stable mounting for the survey.* Clearly, if the antenna is not horizontal or moves during data collection then this will compromise the result.

In addition, there were further requirements set on processing the data, the principal ones being:

1. OS Base Stations would be chosen to give a star network radiating out from the hill to the OS Net stations. This is standard surveying practice.

2. A quality check on the processed result should be carried out via coordinate recovery of the OS Net stations. In this procedure the coordinates of the hill (position and height) are determined by processing the collected two hours of data against the nearest base station. This result for the hill is then used to calculate the coordinates of other base stations which are then compared with the published values. Any differences in height should not be more than 0.1m for base stations less than 100km distant from the hill. For example, when we measured the height of Snowdon we took 12 hours of data and base stations as far away as the Highlands had coordinate recoveries of better than 0.1m. So, the longer the collection time for the dataset then the more robust is the height value determined from it. Conversely, short collection times may give what appears to be a good result, but the precision of the measurement (that is its reproducibility) is poorer.

It should be noted that in the recent survey of the height of Ben Nevis by an Ordnance Survey team of surveyors, this was the exact strategy that the OS team adopted.

It was also agreed with The Munro Society that we would write up each survey into a detailed report. We have heard it said that reports are never read and therefore unnecessary. This view, however, misses the point of a report. The reason for a written report is that it provides a record for posterity of what actually was done; it clarifies misunderstandings that may arise and, if mistakes are found then they can, it is hoped, be rectified or at least understood. If there is no written record of how any piece of technical work has been carried out, then the value of that work is much diminished. It is standard practice in all technical disciplines to issue a detailed report for any serious piece of work. Consequently, we readily agreed to this requirement and indeed it is standard to all the work we do, including surveys we carry out for our own purposes.

Preparation for the Surveys

Before using any piece of equipment it is standard technical practice to demonstrate that it is fit for purpose and functioning correctly and that we understand the associated precision and accuracy of the technique we are employing. What do we mean by precision and what do we mean by accuracy? Imagine throwing nine darts at a dart board and aiming for the bull's eye. For your first go the darts hit the board in random positions. Your aim is neither accurate nor precise. On your next go all nine cluster together in one number. Your aim is very precise (all the darts are clustered tightly together) but not very accurate (you were aiming for the bull). Now let's consider that you have another go and this time you get one in the bull's eye, two in the 25, two in the 20, two in the 3, one in the 6 and one in the 11 with all of the last six being within the triple ring. Although only one actually scored in the bull the average position for the nine darts would be close to the bull, so your third go would be accurate, but not very precise. When you have a fourth go you get all nine in either the bull or the 25. Then your fourth go is both very accurate and very precise. The diagram below illustrates three of these situations.

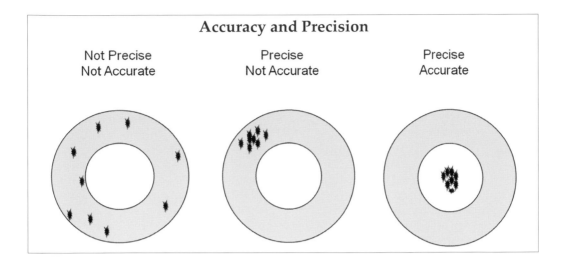

Accuracy and Precision

Not Precise
Not Accurate

Precise
Not Accurate

Precise
Accurate

Standard Deviation

At this point we introduce the term standard deviation. This mathematical term is a way of describing how close, or how scattered, are the individual points in a dataset. For example, in the first of the 'dartboard' pictures above the standard deviation would be large, whereas in the second and third pictures it would be small. For many types of measurement, including GNSS height measurements, a set of many determinations fall on a bell-shaped curve, as shown below, which is termed a normal distribution curve. The mean value is μ which is where the majority of measurement values are likely to fall and as we move along the x-axis in either direction, then successively fewer measurement values will be found in these positions. The symbol σ represents a standard deviation, a specific term represented by a mathematical equation. For our purpose note that successive values, 1 σ, 2 σ and 3 σ are equally spaced around μ. The curve is useful because it tells us how likely it is for a measurement to fall a given distance away from the mean value and the smaller the values of σ then the more tightly packed are measurements likely to be around the mean value, as the two graphs illustrate. In either case it may be seen that 68.2% of the time we would expect a new measurement of height to fall within one standard deviation of the mean value; by the

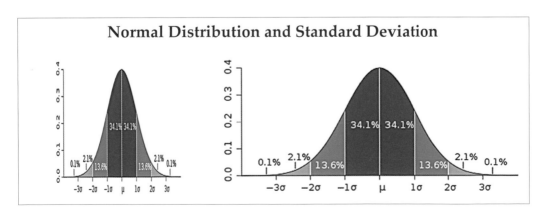

Normal Distribution and Standard Deviation

time we get to three standard deviations, 3 σ, then we might expect a measurement to be found beyond this region of the curve only one time in 400 measurements. So once we know the mean value for a quantity and its standard deviation we can determine how likely it is for any specific value to be measured. For example, there is only a 4.2% chance that a measurement will be made that is beyond 2 σ. If we get two successive measurements that are beyond 2 σ then we should be alerted that something may be wrong with the system we are measuring, as discussed in the next section.

Statistical Quality Control (sqc)

This is a method of determining the precision of measurements made with our GNSS receiver and in particular it helps identify if the instrument is giving spurious results. A convenient position is chosen that has a good view of the sky and twenty height measurements are made with the receiver over a period of weeks. The standard deviation of those measurements is then calculated (for our Leica Viva GS15 receiver this is 0.018m) and a chart is then constructed with lines for one, two and three standard deviations. Further points for data collected at future time intervals are then plotted on the diagram and a moving average (the continuous line) is plotted. The sqc chart for our instrument is shown in the diagram below.

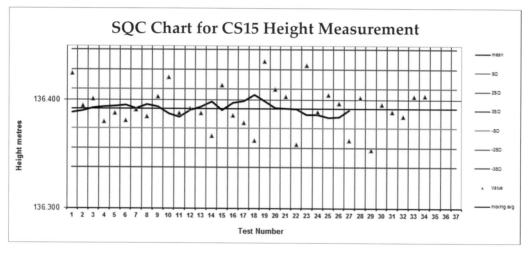

The criteria we use for confirming that our instrument is working properly are:

1. The moving average line remains within the 1SD lines (the green lines in the diagram)
2. No more than two consecutive points are above 2SD (the blue lines)
3. No point is beyond 3SD (the red lines)

If any of these situations occurred then action would be taken to determine why.

Measurements on an Ordnance Survey Benchmark

We periodically take our receiver to an OS fundamental benchmark. This comprises a brass stud set into a sturdy concrete base and the position and height of this benchmark has been measured accurately by OS. There is a network of these benchmarks over the country and one of their functions is to allow surveyors to check the accuracy of their GNSS receivers. The benchmark we use is at Daresbury, just off the M56 and a short drive away. It is convenient to access, since it is on a quiet road leading into the village of Daresbury, and there is parking adjacent to it. The photograph (*right*) shows our second instrument, a Leica Viva GS15, set up over the benchmark and collecting data. The benchmark itself is just visible and comprises a concrete block set into the ground with a brass stud embedded into it. The pole supporting the receiver rests on the stud. We periodically check our Leica Viva GS15 against this benchmark and always before and just after a survey for The Munro Society. Ordnance Survey gives its height as 73.24m and our results have always been between 73.21m and 73.24m. These measurements tell us that the receiver is giving accurate results.

The Leica Viva GS15 at the Daresbury Benchmark

Although a GNSS receiver is a highly reliable instrument, it is sound practice to be able to demonstrate it is in good working order and these measurements enable us to do so.

In a continuation of this work we have made a set of measurements in which two hours of data have been collected for each measurement. The standard deviation of these measurements is 0.018m. Three standard deviations is therefore 0.05m and so we can say that any measurement we make for two hours of data collection will be within +/- 0.05m of the 'correct answer' to 99.8% confidence.

Weather Conditions

Generally, weather conditions have little effect on GNSS measurements, but they can hinder use of the surveyor's level since good visibility is necessary for its use. Even slight mist, that presents no problem to the unaided eye, is sufficient to prevent seeing objects through the level. Wind may also be an issue since strong gusts shake even the sturdiest tripod and the resultant vibration severely hinders the taking of, for example, staff readings. The most testing conditions we encountered were on Beinn Teallach, where we recorded 70mph gusts at the end of the survey. Fortunately, work with level and staff had been completed two hours previously before the wind strengthened. The GNSS receiver was on a sturdy tripod, the legs of which were held down with rocks, but had these gusts hit before the conclusion to data collection then there would have been a strong chance of the whole assembly being blown over. The following day on Ben Vane near Loch Lomond was also as testing, but for a different reason. Here there was mist which prevented us from finding the exact summit position since we were unable to see through the level. GNSS data were collected in the hope that the summit would clear of mist later. Very fortunately this did happen and we were able to confirm the summit position and determine the height difference between it and the GNSS receiver (which turned out to be less than 5m away).

These conditions also provide a test for the surveying party. Shelter on the leeward slope of the mountain provides some respite from the elements, but on our surveys all carried ample clothing and many supplemented this with bivvy bags or survival shelters. There is a big difference between keeping on the move, as on a mountain walk, and sitting still for two hours while the GNSS receiver collects its data.

The Surveys

The start

Our first actions were to agree with the Heightings Coordinator, the hill(s) we were to survey and the dates and venue for the survey. Since the surveys were open to all members of TMS and we, the surveyors, were travelling from the north-west of England, it was not possible to choose dates when the weather would be guaranteed to be fine. This restriction led to some interesting surveys!

The Ascent

On the day we met up at the appointed place and shared the gear between the team. To give an idea of the loads involved our Leica 530 receiver, which we used for many of the surveys, comprised a 5kg back pack containing the data processing unit, two one-metre poles and a receiver weighing about 1kg, a surveyor's level (2.5kg), two tripods (3kg each) and a staff (2.5kg), a total of 17kg. Fortunately, the surveys were well attended by many enthusiastic and fit volunteers and consequently even the most arduous of ascents proved straightforward.

Arrival at the Summit

Once at the summit the first action was to carry out a reconnoitre. All potential high points were noted and examined; could we set up the GNSS receiver over the summit and if not where was best to site it? Were any rocks that were candidates for the summit position really embedded and part of the hill, or were they just loose or partially embedded debris? Was the highest ground under the cairn? Answers to these questions then determined where we set up the surveyor's level and how we conducted the survey.

Use of Level and Staff

A surveyor's level enables the summit area to be surveyed and the heights of the candidate summit features relative to one another to be determined.

To illustrate what the surveyor sees, this photograph is a view taken through the level to the staff, which in this case is about 65m away. The black line crossing near the centre of the picture is the level line. Everything above this line is higher than the telescope of the level and everything below is lower. The staff reading is 1.635m. If the height of the level on the tripod is h metres above the ground then the ground the staff rests on is (1.635 − h) metres lower than the ground the level sits on. For the purpose of finding the highest point of the mountain the value of h is unimportant, since we are finding height differences between different features and so all we need to determine are the staff readings themselves and remember that the higher the staff reading then the lower the feature with respect to its counterparts. The small horizontal lines near the bottom and top of the picture are the stadia lines. These are useful because the apparent distance between them, in this case 0.65m (1.96m − 1.31m), is 1/100 of the distance from the level to the staff which as mentioned above is 65m. Note that a staff reading can easily be read to the nearest millimetre over a distance of 100m, so the level and staff combination is a very powerful one for determining small height differences.

The View through the Leica NA730 Automatic Level

So, once the candidate summit features were identified the level was set up at a convenient position where all were in view. Staff measurements were taken on all these summit candidates and the highest point of the hill determined. Note that this was not always the cairn or trig point. While often occupying the summit, there is no requirement that they do; for example trig points were set up at a convenient position so that other nearby trig points could be observed. It should also be

The Leica NA730 automatic level in action (L Rudkin)

Graham and John locate the highest point (David Batty)

noted that occasionally the nature of the ground, for example a covering of heather or loose soil, can itself introduce an uncertainty in the final height determination (e.g. should detritus under heather be removed or should loose soil be removed before setting up the GNSS receiver?). For higher hills this uncertainty is usually 5cm or less, especially where the summit is rock. Finally, in situations where the GNSS receiver could not be set up over the summit we used the level and staff to determine the height difference between the two positions for later use in the report, as required by Ordnance Survey.

Data Collection

Next the GNSS receiver was set up over the summit (or surveyed position where this was not possible) and data collection commenced. As noted under **Mission Planning** we aimed to do this when there was the maximum number of satellites available in the sky, although many other factors associated with the survey would affect our ability to do this. Nevertheless, collecting data for 2 hours ensured that there were long periods where satellite availability was good. During data collection, photographs were taken of the GNSS receiver as a record of the set-up geometry (see Ordnance Survey requirement 3 above).

Conclusion of survey

Once data collection was completed and the equipment switched off and dismantled, the survey party made its way back down the hill.

Without the willing help of our fellow TMS members to help carry the equipment and their wit and repartee, which helped while away those two hours of data collection, we would have struggled to complete these missions successfully!

Processing the Data

Once back home, the next step was to process the GNSS data we had collected using Leica GeoOffice software. The strategy is described in **Differential GNSS.** First, the data are imported into the software and put into a project which is given the name of the surveyed hill. It is important at this stage to then enter the offset, that is, the height that the receiver was above ground level when set up and operating. Usually, it was either one metre or two metres for the Leica 530 and this is where the photographs taken of the setup are invaluable as a record. Next, data are downloaded from the Ordnance Survey website for the six or seven nearest OS base stations to the hill we had surveyed and for the time period over which our survey data were collected. The exact number of stations used varies with the location of the hill, since surveying practice recommends not selecting base stations further away than 100km. The chosen base stations should also form a star pattern around the survey point, that is, they should be as evenly spaced as possible in a circle around it. The data from the OS base stations is termed RINEX data, which stands for Receiver INdependent EXchange format, a file structure that is recognised universally within the surveying community. The RINEX data are then also imported into Leica GeoOffice and the software told which file is survey data and which files are RINEX data. Finally, GeoOffice is given the computational strategy required. Following from our previous discussion of GNSS technology, we choose only to accept data from satellites that are 15 degrees or more above the horizon. For two hours of GNSS data we also instruct the software to compute its own tropospheric correction from our data, rather than use a proprietary model such as Hopfield. Finally, we instruct the software to process the data and after a few seconds the result is displayed!

Following from our previous discussion, we note that for two hours of GNSS data, measurement uncertainty is +/-0.05m (to three standard deviations). For nearly all of our surveys this was more than acceptable. However, there is specialist software that can process GNSS data to a higher degree of precision. One of these was developed by the University of Bern and, not surprisingly, is called Bernese Software. For many of the surveys and especially where our result would mean that the Ordnance Survey cartography team was instructed to change the height of the hill on OS maps, then our data were processed through this specialist software to give a result with a higher degree of precision, usually +/-1cm. At the same time Ordnance Survey also carried out a Coordinate Recovery analysis to check the robustness of the data collected.

Later in the project we were provided with the spreadsheet by Ordnance Survey to enable us to do this for ourselves as a check, before submitting data to them. A typical Coordinate Recovery is shown in the table below for the survey of Meall Gaineimh, the small top that lies at the east end of the Ben Avon massif and which we surveyed with

The Munro Society in May 2015. The column entitled 'Height Difference' gives the height difference in metres between the quoted height for that base station and the height calculated as described above in '**Standard Requirements of The Munro Society**'. It is seen that for every base station the height difference between the Ordnance Survey value and that calculated from our data (column 4) is less than 0.03m. The column entitled 'Separation Dij metres' is the difference in 3d space between the OS coordinates and the coordinates calculated from our data. Once again all differences are less than 0.03m and well within the 0.1m required.

Base Station	Code	Distance to Survey Point km.	Height Difference U metres	Separation Dij metres
Braemar	BRAE	14		
Inverness	INVR	64	0.007	0.008
Kintore	KINT	66	0.028	0.028
Buckie	BUCK	66	-0.016	0.022
Fort Augustus	FAUG	79	-0.010	0.016
Dundee	DUDE	80	0.004	0.012
Killin	KILN	94	-0.007	0.008

Acknowledgements

We are grateful to Mark Greaves of Ordnance Survey for all the help and encouragement he has given us over the past ten years and for checking and, where appropriate, independently processing our datasets. Where results have differed from map heights Mark has submitted our results to Ordnance Survey Cartography for map changes.

We are also grateful to Leica Geosystems and James Whitworth for first introducing us to GNSS technology and advising on equipment for purchase and to Christopher Gibbons for his continuing and invaluable support and technical advice on operating and maintaining the equipment and associated software. We also thank Leica Geosystems for allowing us to reproduce diagrams for this chapter.

Included in the following table are the results of the earlier surveys by CMCR Ltd. for Foinaven and Beinn Dearg. We are grateful to Jim Melville for supplying the data that enables a complete set of results to be presented in this chapter.

And a big thank you to the TMS Executive for choosing G&J Surveys to carry out the programme of work and to all members of The Munro Society who gave up their time to help with the surveys, by carrying equipment, participating in the work and providing camaraderie during the long periods of data collection, often in bad weather!

The Results of the Surveys

The results of all our surveys for The Munro Society are listed in the table below. The table gives the height measurement for the mountain (recalculated since the release by Ordnance Survey of the latest Geoid model (OSGM15)) and our estimate of the measurement uncertainty of our results (to three standard deviations). We also give the Ordnance Survey value where the data have been processed by Ordnance Survey. We usually quote results to the nearest 0.1m but have given them in the table to the nearest 0.01m in order to allow a comparison with the Ordnance Survey result.

Hill Name	Grid Ref	Height (m) G&J Surveys	Measurement uncertainty (m)	Height (m) OS
Beinn Teallach	NN361859	914.66	+/-0.03	914.62
Ben Vane	NN277098	915.80	+/-0.08	915.77
Sgùrr a' Choire-beithe	NG895015	913.33	+/-0.07	
Sgurr nan Ceannaichean*	NH087480	913.48	+/-0.02	913.45
Geal-charn	NN596782	917.12	+/-0.08	
Beinn a' Chleibh	NN250256	916.32	+/-0.08	
The Fara	NN598842	911.37	+/-0.08	
Beinn a' Chlaidheimh*	NH061775	914.03	+/-0.05	914.01
Beinn Dearg Mòr	NH032799	906.39	+/-0.08	906.34
Ruadh Stac Mòr	NH018756	918.69	+/-0.08	
Leathad a' Taobhain	NN821858	911.71	+/-0.08	
Beinn Bhreac	NN868820	912.44	+/-0.08	
Knight's Peak*	NG471254	914.25	+/-0.06	914.25
Bhàsteir Tooth	NG465252	917.15	+/-0.06	917.17
Carn na Caim S Top*	NN663806	914.62	+/-0.08	
Meall Gaineimh	NJ166051	913.62	+/-0.05	
Foinaven	NC315506	911.08+		
Beinn Dearg	NG895608	913.67+		

* change of status
+ CMCR surveys

Chapter 7

OS Measurement of Ben Nevis

John Barnard and Graham Jackson

Being the highest mountain in Great Britain and Northern Ireland, Ben Nevis is arguably the most important Munro. Although not part of the TMS Heighting project, the height of Ben Nevis had not been accurately measured since the last survey that took place in 1949. Therefore, Ordnance Survey decided to carry out a modern survey using GNSS technology to obtain an accurate height. This was not part of any particular Ordnance Survey project, but it has fitted in with the remeasurement of the highest mountains in Wales and England, that is, Snowdon and Scafell Pike. The former survey was carried out as a joint project between Ordnance Survey and G&J Surveys, which featured as a documentary on ITV Wales in 2015, and the latter was an Ordnance Survey measurement which featured in 2016 on the ITV programme series 'Countrywise'. Like Snowdon, the summit of Ben Nevis bears the scars of human influence and gives the strong impression of untidiness. There are numerous cairns, a raised trig pillar which sits on a cairn and the remains of an old observatory with associated buildings.

The proposal to put an observatory on the summit of Ben Nevis was made in 1877 by David Milne Home. He was chairman of the Council of the Scottish Meteorological Society (SMS) and after a personal ascent to the mountain's summit in 1878 he decided that the plan to build an observatory there was feasible. The plans for its construction were drawn up by an engineer called Thomas Stevenson who invented the 'Stevenson Screen', the instrument shelter designed to protect meteorological instruments from precipitation and direct heat from the sun while allowing air to circulate freely around the instruments. (Incidentally Thomas Stevenson was also the father of the famous author, Robert Louis Stevenson). David Milne Home considered Ben Nevis as a particularly useful site for an observatory as being near the west coast of Scotland it was directly in the line of Atlantic storms.

However, work did not start on the observatory until 1883 when a successful appeal was made for public funds. The appeal was extremely popular with the general public and it had been enhanced by the exploits of Clement Wragge who made many daily ascents of Ben Nevis in all types of weather to obtain meteorological data. The first construction was the 'pony track' to the summit which is now called the 'Tourist Path'. The observatory was officially opened in 1883 by Mrs Cameron Campbell of Monzie estate who ascended the mountain on a pony! Observations from the permanently manned observatory were made for 20 years until its closure in 1904. Despite the importance of the observations, the Scottish Meteorological Society was not able to persuade the Government to cover the annual running costs of £1,000 per annum and hence the reluctant closure and staff dismissal!

The observatory then found another use by becoming a 'summit hotel' where one could be served refreshments. This lasted until 1916 when everything there started to fall into disrepair, a process completed by a fire in 1932. The final straw was that climbers in the 1950s stripped the remains of its building of lead and rolled that down Ben Nevis under the 'excuse' that the money obtained from its sale would finance the 1953 Everest Expedition!

So when Ben Nevis was surveyed in 1949 by Ordnance Survey, how was this carried out? Essentially this was done by making meticulous angle measurements from known positions on other hills. The angle measurements were made using theodolites, each one weighing about 50lbs and that formed part of the 200lbs of equipment that needed to be carried on each ascent and descent of Ben Nevis. This was no easy task and it took a team of seven Ordnance Surveyors 20 consecutive days and nights climbing up and down Ben Nevis in order to make the best possible measurements. Since strong lights were shone towards Ben Nevis from surrounding reference points, for example the trig pillars on Ben Alder, Ben Lawers and Creach Bheinn etc., the surveys had to be carried out at night. In fact during the 20 consecutive days and nights, there were only three nights that were clear enough for measurements to be taken! Not untypical of the weather. The mean result for the height of Ben Nevis from the many measurements made was 1,344m. Unfortunately, the value is rounded to the nearest metre and the actual value obtained in 1949 has been lost. However, one might assume that the height of Ben Nevis would have to be less than 1,344.500m to be rounded down.

A typical OS survey in the 1940s (Copyright OS)

In 2015 it was noticed that the cairn supporting the trig pillar was becoming undermined and therefore potentially unstable. This was due primarily to the adverse weather on the summit but large numbers of feet at that point for the summit photographs also played a major contribution. The necessary repair work was carried out by a partnership of the John Muir Trust and the Nevis Landscape Partnership. The sides of the cairn were rebuilt and so were the set of steps that leads up to the platform surrounding the trig pillar. This work was funded jointly by Ordnance Survey, the John Muir Trust and Heritage Lottery.

The Heighting of Ben Nevis was carried out by Ordnance Survey using the same methods it recommended to G&J Surveys for all the surveys in the TMS Heightings Project, methods that G&J Surveys adopted for the Project. Although the platform surrounding the trig pillar is about 2 - 3m higher than the base, this area is not considered to be the highest point since it is on man-made ground. The natural summit, which is higher than the base of the cairn, is a short distance away from it and was identified using an automatic level and staff. However, the Leica GS15 GNSS receiver was attached to the spider of the trig pillar and two hours of GNSS data were collected. Therefore, a height correction was needed using the automatic level and staff from the top of the trig pillar to the natural summit. Modern technology is a lot simpler than the methods employed in 1949! The equipment is a lot lighter and not subject to the weather conditions except for the safety aspect of trying to do any survey in high winds. Also, apart from the optical work to locate the summit position with automatic level and staff, visibility is not a problem. In fact, apart from the ascent and descent, the survey probably took three surveyors about three hours, a large improvement on 20 days! The accuracy of the final result would also be much improved.

Finding the highest point on Ben Nevis under typical conditions (Copyright OS)

The next stage in the survey is 'back to the laboratory' where the GNSS data has to be processed. Instead of using adjacent trig pillars as in the 1949 survey, the height of Ben Nevis is measured relative to the network of Ordnance Survey fixed GNSS Base stations. Ordnance Survey uses the state of the art Bernese software, developed at the University of Bern in Switzerland. Although in principle this software is similar to that available to G&J Surveys, that is Leica GeoOffice, it has a much higher degree of sophistication in its modelling of the GNSS data which allows more accurate results to be obtained. However, these differences are quite small and if we compare heights where we have the same GNSS data processed with both GeoOffice and Bernese software the heights differ by no more than 4cm.

*The Leica Viva
GS15 collecting
data on the trig
pillar on Ben Nevis
(Copyright OS)*

So, what was the surveyed height for Ben Nevis? The quoted answer is 1,344.527m. (Although this is quoted to the nearest mm it is more realistic to round it to 1,344.53m). As explained in the section on Geoid Models this uses the new UK Geoid model OSGM15, as Ordnance Survey were aware that this new model was to replace OSGM02 later in 2016. Therefore, it is the most up to date height. For Ben Nevis the change in the height due to the different Geoid models is very small at 7mm. As Ordnance Survey quotes heights on its maps to the nearest metre, then the height will be written as 1,345m. In fact, there is an additional subtlety on the 1:50,000 and 1:25,000 scale maps that two heights will be quoted. One will be 1,344m, which is the height of the base of the cairn supporting the trig pillar, and in brackets next to that will be 1,345m as the rounded height of the highest natural point.

Once Ordnance Survey had announced the result of the survey the Daily Press seized on the fact that Ben Nevis had increased in height and, because of the rounding, the figure of 1m was often quoted. But exactly what was the difference between the 2016 and 1949 surveys? As stated earlier the unrounded number for the height obtained in the 1949 survey has been lost but assuming it was a maximum of 1,344.500m to justify the rounding down to 1,344m, then the measured height difference could be as little as approximately 3cm. Of course it could be almost a metre different if the 1949 measured height were 1,343.501m as this still would justify the rounding to 1,344m. However, what is extremely important is how good the 1949 survey measurement was and what a fantastic job those surveyors did with much less sophisticated equipment than we have at our disposal today!

Chapter 8

Members' Reflections on the Further Heightings

David Batty

TMS members played an important part in the Heightings. Derek Sime and Glen Breaden have already provided their reflections of the first Heightings of Beinn Dearg and Foinaven. In this chapter I, along with Derek Sime and Eleanore Hunter, share our reflections on the further Heightings carried out by G & J Surveys.

I joined the Munro Society in 2009 after the Heightings programme was already underway. I had recently lost my wife to cancer and was looking to re-focus my life. Little was I to realise on joining how much the Munro Society was going to do just that and in such a rewarding way. The Heightings brought me into close contact from an early date with many of the more active members and I was soon integrating into the Heightings calendar and the various Society meets and events. In those early days I had no idea how many friendships I was to form and how much camaraderie pervaded throughout the Society's activities. The Heightings were particularly special as everyone joined together on the hill in a common purpose, on occasions braved harsh elements together, often socialised in the evenings and shared the anticipation of the unknown outcome.

Beinn Teallach and Ben Vane

I attended the third Heighting on Beinn Teallach on 15th May 2009. That was a baptism of fire, or I should say wind. I had ventured onto the hills a few times in extremely

Gale on Beinn Teallach May 2009 (TMS Archive)

windy conditions, even turned back on Ben Lawers in the face of an irresistible force, and been blown off my feet on Creach Bheinn. The wind at the summit that day was constantly around 50 to 60mph and one particularly fierce gust topped 70mph. It is one thing to keep moving on the hill in such conditions but by the time we had located the highest point, set up the equipment, gathered the data and packed up, we had been at the summit for around three hours. There were many freezing bodies and hands as we waited at the summit, taking turns to guard the equipment and ensure there was no movement which would lead to restarting or even abandoning the survey. It was a great introduction to seeing how Graham and John, ably assisted by Myrddyn, went about the survey and how meticulous they were in locating the precise summit point, setting up the equipment and gathering the data. That was the first of several occasions when we found the cairn not to be at the highest point. I can't recall having to carry any equipment up on that day, such joy lying ahead! On future Heightings I was to find that on calmer days there was time to walk out to a nearby subsidiary top or even another Munro or Corbett. I was pursuing a second Munro round at that time but there was no question in that wind and with all hands on deck of walking over to Beinn a' Chaorainn. My abiding memory of the Beinn Teallach Heighting, however, is the great spirit among the group who stoically braved the fierce conditions to ensure the equipment remained stable and the survey was completed, and at the same time had a good laugh at the conditions faced.

The next Heighting took place on the following day on Ben Vane. Unfortunately I couldn't attend and Derek Sime takes up the story –

> Being gainfully employed at the time, I couldn't make it to the day on Beinn Teallach, being a Friday, but as the team planned to follow it up with a visit to Ben Vane on the Saturday, I decided to lend some assistance as a porter. It

The Party at Inveruglas: Derek Sime, Fred Ward, Graham Jackson, Iain Robertson, John Barnard, Myrddyn Phillips, Angus Campbell, John Ross and Peter Willimott (©Myrddyn Phillips)

was 16th May 2009.

Since my previous experiences on Foinaven and Beinn Dearg, the surveyors had changed, and John and Graham were both very experienced hill men, and very hill-fit. So, far from our crack-of-dawn starts on these earlier hills, the team arranged to start at the positively leisurely hour of 09:30. We all met up at the car park at Inveruglas, on the western shore of Loch Lomond, four miles north of Tarbet, and took the usual route to the summit. There were nine of us on this occasion, those who had heighted Beinn Teallach the day before looking remarkably fresh after their ordeal.

Beinn Ime and Ben Vane (Derek Sime)

Being accustomed to what I will call 'Heighting weather', expectations were not optimistic for wall-to-wall sunshine and blue sky, and we were not to be disappointed in that respect, particularly as the team had enjoyed gale force winds and worse the previous day on Beinn Teallach. The weather was overcast, with a cloud base of around 500m (very reminiscent of the Beinn Dearg Heighting in fact), although by mid-afternoon, it had lifted to nearer 900m. The visibility was down to 20m at times, with occasional showers, some quite heavy. The brisk southerly wind caused some buffeting, not to mention chilling during the long wait at the summit. So, situation normal then.

Despite that, spring was in evidence if you looked hard enough, with primroses, purple saxifrage and wild hyacinth in flower, and the sound of chattering chaffinches and swallows. A ptarmigan was heard at about 750m, but only seen by one member of the group, presumably on account of the mist.

The weather, Ben Vane (©Myrddyn Phillips)

But then it was down to business at the summit, the first job being to identify exactly where the summit was. Some traditional surveying in the mist with staff and level eventually identified the highest point, on rock, some 50m to the north-west of the (assumed summit) cairn, and close to a second cairn. This had proved time consuming on account of the mist, as even with fairly short spacing, it proved difficult to read the staff. Then came the customary two hour wait – no opportunity this time to run along a ridge to visit an outlying Top, Corbett or second Munro; there was no option but to sit it out, no matter how uncomfortable the experience in the prevailing conditions. Two hours can seem a very long time in such circumstances. A good number of hill walkers came and went during that time, some curious as to our purpose, others not. When told that the cairn was not at the highest point, again some took note and visited the 'new' summit while others, clearly thinking we were totally mad, were satisfied that a visit to the cairn would qualify for the obligatory tick in the book.

Once all the necessary measurements had been taken for the requisite time, we all packed up, the loads were distributed to the porters, and we trotted off back down, retracing our outward route. Another Heighting in the bag, we treated ourselves to a light refreshment in the Tarbet Hotel before heading our separate ways. The result was announced some weeks later, and Ben Vane had retained its (albeit marginal) Munro status.

Sgùrr a' Choire-bheithe and Sgùrr nan Ceannaichean

I attended the next trip to Sgùrr a' Choire-bheithe and Sgùrr nan Ceannaichean two months later in July 2009. At the time the former was a Corbett and the latter a Munro

The party disembarking at Barisdale for Sgùrr a' Choire-bheithe (TMS Archive)

and I still needed to climb both for the rounds I was pursuing. I always enjoyed the Heighting trips for their own sake but to be able to add to my rounds at the same time was an added bonus. As I had purchased a small one-man tent to use on trips for my second Munro round I decided to camp the previous night close to Arnisdale. Arrangements had been made to sail across Loch Hourn the following morning to Barrisdale Bay in Billy Mackenzie's boat. After the long journey north and the drive over the Màm Ratagan I was starting to think that a comfortable bed for the night would be more welcome than the tent but enquiries at a couple of B&Bs proved fruitless. So, camping it was. I found a delightful spot on a high point looking down on Arnisdale with Loch Hourn stretched out beside me and the Cuillin to the west and pitched the tent. At the second B&B I had tried at Corran I had had a really good piece of luck. It was occupied by Stewart Logan and Peter Willimott and, having met Peter at the Beinn Teallach Heighting, they invited me to join them for dinner in Glenelg. A further bonus was that I didn't have to drive. So, what looked like being a solitary evening and early night was anything but, being spent in most convivial company. The evening ended with a beautiful sunset over the Isle of Skye. I was up and about very early the next morning and was soon being pestered by midges. I walked over to look at Loch Hourn and saw the amazing sight of a pod of dolphins making their way up the loch. Sadly my camera wasn't to hand and I lost the moment. After breakfast and with plenty of time to fill I walked down to the foreshore. There wasn't a breath of wind, the tide was on the turn and the seaweed a rich brown and gold. Boats sat serenely in Camas Bàn and across the loch mist floated over the tops of Ladhar Bheinn, Luinne Bheinn and the target for the day, Sgùrr a' Choire-bheithe.

Sgùrr a' Choire Bheithe and Luinne Bheinn across a serene Loch Hourn (David Batty)

As the party assembled at the pier it was obvious that two trips would be required. I managed to join Graham and John in the first boat which also carried another party who had booked the boat to drop them off for an ascent of Ladhar Bheinn. It meant Graham and John could save time by getting on with their survey to establish the highest point before the others arrived. Compared to the rather fraught and frantic proceedings on gale-swept Beinn Teallach it was good to see how the whole cycle of the Heighting process was carried out with Graham and John incredibly patient as they explained what they were doing and the complex science behind it. From that knowledge gained it always amused me on later occasions when the doubters came out of the woodwork not understanding how thorough, careful and competent

John Barnard sets up the gear on Sgùrr a' Choire-bheithe (Iain A. Robertson)

Above: Sgùrr nan Ceannaichean (David Batty)

Below: Summit party on Sgùrr a' Coire-bheithe: David Batty, Iain Robertson, David Cran, Peter Willimott, Alistair Milner, Stewart Logan, Graham Jackson and John Barnard
(© Myrddyn Phillips)

Graham and John were and the sophisticated equipment they were using.

What became a familiar pattern emerged when Graham and John were rather coy about the likely result. They may often have had a gut feel on the hill before the data are processed, but until this is done and, furthermore, approved by Ordnance Survey, and the result conveyed to our Heightings co-ordinator Iain Robertson, we ordinary mortals were kept in the dark. Nobody doubted that was how it should be. The mist hung around all day although good views were had from time to time particularly that stunning view across Loch Hourn to Beinn Sgritheall. It turned out to be a long day and we weren't back at the pier at Arnisdale until 6pm. The party then headed for Ratagan Youth Hostel where a booking had been made for the night ahead of the Heighting of Sgùrr nan Ceannaichean the following day.

I had last stayed at Ratagan Youth Hostel more than 45 years previously and memories of the visit although sketchy are pleasant. I was there with a friend and one walk we did was up Strath Croe and over the Bealach na Sròine to the Falls of Glomach on a day of low cloud and rain. I remember little except that, as we relaxed at the Falls, a cat appeared. Too inexperienced then to be sure whether it was a true wildcat or a feral cat, I have often wondered since if I had the rare privilege of seeing a wildcat in the wild. The experience this time was in stark contrast. The dormitory was full and the windows were shut on a warm clammy night to keep the midges out. I recall an almost sleepless night and waking up very early with a great desire to abandon the dormitory which I duly did. I headed down to the shore of Loch Duich for a walk. It was another great photo opportunity. The mountain tops were clear but wisps of mist floated across the loch which rippled in the slight welcoming breeze. I could see across to the Five Sisters

A' Ghlas-bheinn across Loch Duich (David Batty)

Above: On Sgùrr nan Ceannaichean the cairn was not at the highest point (©Myrddyn Phillips)

Right: Graham Jackson, getting it just right! (David Batty)

and Sgùrr an Airgid and further to the serrated north-west ridge of Beinn Fhada and the slopes of A' Ghlas-bheinn. Memories of some past ascents floated with the mist. Returning to the dormitory I was overpowered by the 'aroma' as I opened the door and decided to head off without further delay.

I stopped in a parking area beside Loch Carron and got the stove going for a brew. Before I knew it, time had flown by and I had to drive rather too quickly to get to the rendezvous for Sgùrr nan Ceannaichean on time. The hills were clear and rain stayed away although high cloud hung around all day. Graham and John went through the now more familiar routines and we all relaxed on the summit. Some of the party headed off to climb Moruisg while the data were being collected. Two young female walkers appeared and took an interest in what was going on and Alistair Milner explained it all to them. During the various Heightings walkers would occasionally pass through although on most occasions I recall no one did. Some were interested and others weren't, just moving on with hardly a word. By the time we had got down off the mountain I was getting rather weary from too little sleep and, mindful of the long drive home, declined the invitation to join the party at the local hotel. It had been a marvellous two days. What was missing at that stage was knowledge of the outcome of the two Heightings. I attended the subsequent press conference to announce that Sgùrr nan Ceannaichean was to be re-classified as a Corbett. That wasn't really what we wanted, much preferring to announce Sgùrr a' Choire-bheithe as a new Munro. But, such is life. I was pleased at the use of the term re-classification, however, as I dislike all the usual references to promoting and demoting hills as if they were football teams entering or leaving the Premier Division.

Geal-charn, Beinn a' Chlèibh and The Fara

I attended the three Heightings carried out in 2010 on Geal-charn, Beinn a' Chlèibh and The Fara. The first of these was in April on Geal-charn at Drumochter. The party met at Balsporran Cottages in, for once, splendid weather, and I recall a really enjoyable occasion. I had finally graduated to being trusted to carry equipment, the rather cumbersome tripod, to the summit. John and Graham were no slouches on the hill and liked to ensure that the equipment they needed arrived at the top with them to avoid delays in carrying out the survey. John always carried the pole. The favourite 'load' was getting to carry John and Graham's sandwiches for them! This was the first occasion that I came in contact with the 'Willimott hill sandwich', a matter of much hilarity at the time.

This Heighting could have been abandoned before it started as not long after we arrived at Balsporran Cottages there was a serious accident at Drumochter Pass and the police stopped the traffic flow for most of the time we were at the summit. That Heighting was also significant for me as during the proceedings Iain Robertson and Peter Willimott asked me if I would like to join the TMS Committee.

Eleanore Hunter also attended this Heighting and has a vivid recollection of it –

> It was a beautiful spring day with high wispy cloud and long sunny spells. There was a magnificent view down to Loch Ericht and some time was spent discussing the merits or otherwise of the new build at Ben Alder Lodge. The bright yellow colour was in stark contrast to the surrounding area and seemed strangely out of place. We remembered Geordie Oswald who had been the gate-keeper at Dalwhinnie and from whom we were required to collect the key to gain entry to the hinterland beyond. We marvelled at the views, the Fara in the near north and the Monadh Liath beyond and in the west to Ben Alder Forest and across to the Creag Meagaidh Nature Reserve. A small group of us including Iain Robertson and David Cran walked round to A' Mharconaich and back in time to pack up the equipment and begin the descent.

The SMC Raeburn Hut was booked for the end of July, the party on that occasion

The car park at Balsporran, Geal-charn behind: Iain Robertson, David Batty, David Cran, Eleanore Hunter, Myrddyn Phillips, Stewart Logan, Charles Murray, Peter Willimott, John Barnard and Graham Jackson (Jim Melville),

meeting first beside the A85 in Glen Lochy to undertake the Heighting of Beinn a' Chlèibh. The instructions issued by Iain Robertson stated 'for those who have not previously attended a Heighting be prepared in terms of clothing, food and water for three plus hours at the summit'. More prophetic words of advice could not have been offered. Of all the Heightings I attended that one was the most uncomfortable. Fortunately, I had brought my Gore-Tex bivvy bag and spent most of the time at the summit shivering in its inner recesses, a salutary reminder that even in July it can be seriously cold and miserable if one gets stuck on a Scottish mountain. Once we had settled into the Raeburn Hut and refuelled with a hot meal all that was soon forgotten and a convivial evening followed. The following day we tackled the Fara, walking in from Loch Ericht. I had been able to add Beinn a' Chlèibh to my Munro tally but had already climbed the Fara via the Dirc Mhòr.

Above: Peter Willimott with his hill sandwich (David Batty)

Below: Walter McArthur makes the best of it on Beinn Teallach (Iain A Robertson)

The Fara, of course, has an enormous cairn at its summit, except we soon found that it wasn't at the summit but quite a few yards away. It was just as well, as to dismantle that cairn and rebuild it wasn't on the agenda. On the Heightings I attended we never had to dismantle a cairn and the cairn on most occasions wasn't at the exact summit. Fortunately the weather had improved from the previous day although photographs show the party well wrapped up in woolly hats, gloves and over-trousers. I stayed a further night at the Raeburn hut and was able to climb the two most westerly Tops of Creag Meagaidh the following day. By this time I had attended six Heightings and had made a number of friends and close acquaintances along the way. I had no intention of missing any future Heightings but that depended on funds being available for them to continue.

The Fara ridge looking south (Iain A. Robertson)

The Heighting Party on The Fara:
back, Stewart Logan, Alistair Milner, Fred Ward, Charles Murray, Peter Willimott, John Ross;
front, David Batty, Graham Jackson and Myrddyn Phillips (Iain A. Robertson)

The Fisherfield Heightings

Thanks to the generosity of Society member, Lord Alan Haworth of Fisherfield, funds were made available to carry out three Heightings in Fisherfield Forest in 2011. This was a superb multi-day trip in fabulous surroundings from an ideal base at the Sàil Mhòr hostel and for me the pinnacle of the enjoyment these occasions brought. It was the first time I had approached Fisherfield from the west and it was very special. Details are described in Chapter 9 by Myrddyn Phillips but on the trip to Ruadh Stac Mòr I was able to undertake an additional objective. On joining the Munro Society committee Glen Breaden had asked me to take on the role of Mountain Reporting Co-ordinator.[1] This entailed contributing to and keeping a database of reports on various aspects of the mountain ascended. As the experience a mountain offers varies by season, reports were being sought for each of the four seasons. As it happened A' Mhaighdean didn't have a Mountain Quality Indicator (MQI) report for the summer so by continuing on from Ruadh Stac Mòr once the survey was set up and data collection under way I was able to complete a report.

Ruadh Stac Mòr, A' Mhaighdean and Beinn Lair (Derek Sime)

As I waited beside Fuar Loch Mòr for the party to descend Ruadh Stac Mòr I was treated to a marvellous display of dancing diamonds as the breeze gently rippled the surface of the loch and the sun sparkled. That was one of the best half-hours I have ever spent in the Scottish hills. The other memory I have of that occasion was of being trusted by John and Graham with carrying the GPS all the way from Kernsary to the top of Ruadh Stac Mòr. However, as it weighed in at around five kilos I wondered if it would have been better to be less trustworthy!

Of course on that trip Beinn a' Chlaidheimh was also re-classified as a Corbett, leading some wags in the Munro Society to re-title the Heightings as the Lowerings. Eleanore was present at the Fisherfield Heightings and provides her reflections –

---

1   At the time, this was concerned with Mountain Quality Indicators (MQIs), a project which ran from 2003 until 2015, after which it was superseded by the Mountain Reports project, which is ongoing, the purpose of this project being to monitor the state of our mountains over time. Reports can be viewed at www.tmsmountainreports.net.

Above: Summit party on Ruadh Stac Mòr: Graham Jackson, Alan Brook, John Barnard, Glen Breaden and Myrddyn Phillips (Iain A. Robertson)

Below: The Heighting gear on Ruadh Stac Mòr, looking to A' Mhaighdean (Iain A. Robertson)

For me the Heighting that stands out like a beacon was that of Beinn a' Chlaidheimh in the Fisherfield Forest, one of the Fisherfield Six (at the time). We got up at some unearthly time of the morning and having divided up the various bits of equipment we were soon on our way. I left Sàil Mhòr Croft saying that I doubted whether I would be able to keep on carrying the extra weight all day. My pack felt very heavy. It was a beautiful morning, ideal walking conditions and the party made good progress, arriving at the summit about the expected time. Once there I lay back and enjoyed the sunshine until Myrddyn Phillips asked for an interview. I found myself having to answer questions on topics related to mountains and the Munro

Above: On the causeway between the Fionn Loch and the Dubh Loch: David Batty, Alan Brook, Graham Jackson and John Barnard (Glen Breaden)

Right: David (r) handing over the GPS to Graham (l) on Ruadh Stac Mòr (TMS Archive)

Society. This interview appeared on YouTube with my cousin making encouraging remarks such as 'It's not too bad'. I remember feeling that this day was unbelievable. I had, of course, been there before when I compleated the round of six in 1996 some 15 years earlier but I never expected to be there again. The walk out was amazing but still extremely hot and I was certainly dehydrated. Eventually we reached the road and the hostel. It was like a magical fairy-tale come true. I had not even noticed the extra weight of the equipment.

The ascent of Beinn Dearg Mòr, also in Fisherfield and a couple of days later, was altogether different. We stopped at Shenavall on the way in as some of the group had slept there the night before. At least one member had to retreat along the way as the pace proved too much. This time I was not an official member of the party but I had offered to be backstop and arrived at the summit in the last group shortly before the equipment was dismantled, the necessary data having been collected. We were soon on our way back. One or two folk took a wrong turning on the return route and had to be hastily redirected. We stopped again at Shenavall to retrieve belongings and around that time the party became too spread out for comfort. We did not actually

Above: The summit of Beinn a' Chlaidheimh looking to An Teallach (©Myrddyn Phillips)

Below: The party at Shenavall, Beinn Dearg Mòr in the background: standing, Fred Ward, Susan Sharpe, Alex Thomson, David Batty, Eleanore Hunter, Graham Jackson, Peter Willimott, Alan Haworth, John Barnard, John Rogerson; kneeling, John Ross, Angus Campbell, Myrddyn Phillips (Iain A. Robertson)

lose anyone but it was very late before the last members appeared. Weather-wise the day had not been so kind, being misty and drizzly for part of the time but it was good enough for our purposes.

Another late arrival at Sàil Mhòr Croft and a late meal. Here is a memory from that day. No matter how dehydrated you may be there are just some things you will not do. Although there were little pools of water on the summit they were considered unsuitable for drinking purposes as unmentionable things were said to be taking place in them. Better the devil you know and all that...

Above: Fisherfield, July 2011 (Iain A Robertson)

Left: Heighting the sub-top of Beinn Dearg Mòr (Iain A. Robertson)

Below: The summit party on Beinn Dearg Mòr (TMS Archive)

Leathad an Taobhain and Beinn Bhreac

I didn't attend the Gaick Heightings of Leathad an Taobhain and Beinn Bhreac in June 2012. I was closing in on completing my round of Corbetts and had become rather single-minded. As I had already climbed those two hills I decided to leave them to others. Also, because of the distances involved permission had been granted to take a 4WD vehicle which would transport the surveyors and their equipment. I felt there wasn't the same need for a support party and the group was going to be split up without the same closeness on the long walk in as I had experienced on the Fisherfield Heighting.

Eleanore was present at the Leathad an Toabhain Heighting and provides her somewhat chilling reflections –

> The ascent of Leathad an Taobhain was an altogether different matter. The main party was staying in the Raeburn Hut but as it was rather cramped I opted to stay with Anne Butler in comfort in Aviemore and we drove down to the start in convoy. It was a miserable day with low cloud and rain and wind on the summit plateau. I was lucky enough to hitch a lift in the Land Rover which took us well up the track. We passed a yellow bundle which was rolling about on the ground. Peter Willimott emerged from this bundle cold but eager to press on. We made our way to the summit plateau where the weather was foul. After a short time, fearing the onset of hypothermia, two of us were ordered off the hill. Despite protesting, that was not an order to be defied, so reluctantly we began the descent but ended up almost running down the track to get warm. I recovered quickly enough and drove down the A9 to get to Stirling for my Book Group that evening. I heard later that the return downhill by the bikers was so fast that one member, who shall remain nameless, broke his bike by sustaining a buckled wheel, although it was still usable (just) next day on Beinn Bhreac.

Leathad an Taobhain – and then the mist came down (Iain A. Robertson)

Derek attended the Beinn Bhreac Heighting and picks up that story –

Three years passed before I was able to join another Heighting, as most had been arranged for mid-week. Once again, the heighters were out on the Friday, measuring Leathad an Taobhain, with Beinn Bhreac planned for Saturday 16th June, 2012. Judging that the track would be too rough for my road bike, and not possessing a mountain bike at the time, I had hired one for the weekend. To avoid a red-eye start, I drove up to Blair Atholl on the Friday evening after work, and booked into a local B & B, although as we all know, no self-respecting Highland establishment serves breakfast before 8 o'clock, especially on a Saturday, so a breakfast tray was delivered to the room in the evening. Despite the fitness of the surveyors, this was going to be a long day, and we had arranged to meet at Calvine at 07:00 sharp, although by the time all had arrived it was a not-so-sharp quarter to eight! The first seven miles or so were to be undertaken by mountain bike, along the estate road as far as Bruar Lodge, and then a further mile, to Allt Beinn Losgarnaich, where we left the bikes. Being uphill, that took 1¾ hours (we probably could have just about walked it in that time). At one point we were overtaken by Anne and Bill Butler's Range Rover, conveying the surveyors and at least one of the porters who had somehow

Above: Leathad an Taobhain – lying down on the job! (Iain A. Robertson)

On the Beinn Bhreac Heighting – Iain Robertson, John Rogerson and Stewart Logan (Derek Sime)

managed to hitch a lift (names withheld to avoid embarrassment!). At the end of the bike section, we met up with the occupants of the Range Rover, and the loads were distributed for a carry to the summit.

From there, fully laden, we continued on foot up the stalkers' path on the right bank of Allt Beinn Losgarnaich, continuing north-east and descending to the headwaters of the Tarf Water at NN858810 (the bog section), finally climbing north-east to the summit of Beinn Bhreac. Once again, we had good 'Heighting weather' – the usual cocktail of an overcast sky, a low cloud base (700m on this occasion) frequent light drizzle and this time, just for variety, a cool east wind. The surveyors got down to the business in hand without delay while the rest of us sought what shelter we could find on the somewhat bleak summit. Some took to make-shift shelters and bivvy bags, while others (the author included) settled down to enjoy the view through the mist for two hours, occasionally walking round in ever decreasing circles in an attempt to keep the circulation going, just a few days short of the summer solstice.

The work complete, bivvy bags folded up, rucksacks packed, we set off down by our outward route, except that we took a diversion over spot height 786m, at NN839788, to the south-east of Lochan Mon an Fhidhain, an un-named 'top' and rather insignificant to most, but apparently of great significance to some.

It must have been one of the longest Heighting days, distance-wise, yet ironically we completed it three hours quicker than the short walk to and from Beinn Dearg five years previously. The total distance was 23 miles (15 of which were cycled), with a total ascent of 970m (of which 380m were cycled). Happily the downhill cycle took just under an hour. Due to work commitments this ended my involvement in the Heightings.

Sitting it out on the summit of Beinn Bhreac – Colin Walter and Alistair Milner (Derek Sime)

The Skye Heightings

In 2013 I attended the Heighting of Knight's Peak. This was organised by Alistair Milner, who had taken over as co-ordinator from Iain Robertson, ably assisted by Alistair's wife Beryl. The Croft Bunkhouse at Portnalong was used as the base. This was the first time SMC had been involved in the actual Heighting which I found to be a very encouraging development. I had been rather annoyed when our exploits had been described as 'shenanigans' although the most recent description of 'irrepressible heighters' shows how perceptions have moved on. Technically the Heighting of Knight's Peak was a far more difficult proposition. I was aware of this as I had been guided on to it twice before on a traverse of Pinnacle Ridge and a winter ascent up the gully between the third and fourth pinnacles. The addition of one of Scotland's leading climbers, SMC Past President Andy Nisbet, was therefore a very welcome presence. On this trip the Bhàsteir Tooth was also heighted but I chose to head to the north of Skye to climb two Grahams. This was a decision I regretted later when I decided to compleat a second round of Munro Tops. Both these Heightings are described by Myrddyn Phillips in Chapter 9.

Looking down on Knight's Peak (David Batty)

Eleanore was also on the Heightings trip to Skye and provides some poignant memories of Alistair Milner –

> The Skye Heighting was a joint effort between SMC and TMS. Alistair Milner had recently been appointed Heighting Co-ordinator and at that time had become very unwell. Although he and his wife Beryl were to be responsible

for the catering I offered to help. This was quickly accepted and so I set off on the long road to Skye leaving behind the Norwegian branch of my family a day early. Just as well I went, as Alistair had been admitted to hospital the night before. I was not on the Cuillin at all as my knees were not behaving and it was too risky. However, I did manage a Marilyn with Alistair and Beryl the following day but was shocked by Alistair's condition.

After the Skye Heightings the Munro Society effectively called a halt to the original programme. I attended the two further Heightings on Meall Gaineimh and Carn na Caim South Top and was joined by Eleanore on the latter –

My last Heighting was to the south top of Carn na Caim. Three of us left Stirling in the morning and arrived at the parking spot to join the others. This was an uneventful day by comparison with the other Heightings I attended. We walked up the well-constructed path where the obligatory photos were taken, and hung around while the necessary data were accumulated, stamping our feet to keep warm. Then three of us left to find a hostelry that would serve chips and a pint of beer while the surveyors and others stayed to measure another feature.

Reflecting on my involvement in the Heightings I remember the cold on some of the summits – bone chilling definitely, the memory of that cold will never leave me. The camaraderie, the shared love of the hills, the fun and laughter, the nonsense of it all – the professionalism of the surveyors – the beauty and drama of the settings – the accommodation of and towards one another. The strong ties that were forged leading to permanent friendships.

Carn na Caim – Find the bump (Iain A. Robertson)

In some respects completion of the Heightings left a hole in the social activities of the Society. Over the years around 45 people attended, of whom 33 were TMS members. I will always see it as one of the most enjoyable activities I have been involved in. New friends made, marvellous locations visited, sociable days and evenings enjoyed, an increased awareness of the issues involved in defining and measuring the mountains and being a part, albeit a very small part, of the Heighting of Scotland's mountains. Eleanore, ever mindful of others, made sure we didn't forget the deaths of six people who were on these expeditions and are now no longer with us (Irvine Butterfield, Ian Collie, David Cran, Bob Kyle, Walter McArthur and Alistair Milner). This is a sobering thought and lends poignancy to these outings.

The author wishes to thank Eleanore Hunter and Derek Sime for their contributions to this Chapter.

Chapter 9

A Welshman's Observations on the Heightings

Myrddyn Phillips

Since my first excursions into the Welsh mountains, I can recall many special times and so many vivid experiences. Days when the colour almost screams out to be touched, and those quieter moments when one looks down on the intricacies of life at one's feet, with details of colour and movement in small pools, or blades of grass being delicately blown, or when the beauty of an ice crystal reflects a myriad of colour. All of these have been savoured and more. Wales is blessed with some of the finest scenery in the whole of Britain; it has an abundance of variety to its uplands from the rock carved giants of its north, to the open wilderness of its central heartlands to the old red sandstone hills of its south. I have walked all, but still only know a fraction of what the country has to offer.

However, the topographic merit of these beautiful Isles of ours is dominated by the Scottish hills. The sheer quantity and quality of the Highlands surpass other parts of Britain, and although my native Wales has led me into the hills I soon ventured north and experienced magical days on Britain's highest, Ben Nevis, and traversed the Tarmachan Ridge, which although bathed in mist was in full winter refinement. But few hill memories match that of arriving at the summit of Ben Lawers in the late light of a winter's day, and which proved a bewitching experience as daylight quickly ebbed to frost encrusted moonlight where snow-bound peaks laid out in alpenglow shone like bejewelled lights in a northern sky. Soon after visiting Ben Lawers and due to other commitments my trips north became less frequent and it was only a chance meeting that led me to the fine art of surveying a hill and the prospect for future Scottish forays.

Surveying the Hills

My surveying activities started through a chance meeting with Dewi Jones in the high car park at Bwlch y Groes. He had just returned from the hills toward the main Aran ridge, whilst I had paid a quick visit to Moel y Cerrig Duon. Approaching Dewi I noticed a copy of the Nuttalls' Welsh guide to the 2,000ft mountains in the boot of his car, and during the subsequent conversation Dewi informed me that he had recently found a new 2,000ft peak on top of Cnicht. This news filled me with excitement and a little alarm, as if true it meant a bit of catching up was needed to bring my Welsh 2,000ft round total up to date.

If the drop value of the hill Dewi had found was confirmed, it would qualify for inclusion in the list of English and Welsh 2,000ft mountains compiled by John and Anne Nuttall, which have criteria of 2,000ft minimum height and 15m minimum drop.[1] The drop value of a hill is also referred to as prominence or re-ascent and applies to the height difference between the summit and connecting col to the next higher summit along the watershed. In recent times minimum drop values for hills such as those qualifying

---

1   John & Anne Nuttall: *The Mountains of England & Wales*, Vol. I, Wales, Cicerone Guide, 2009

for the Nuttalls' List are written as P15, with the P standing for Prominence and the 15 denoting the minimum drop value of 15m.

Dewi explained how he had measured this hill's drop by attaching a spirit level to his walking staff at a one metre height level; he'd also recently met John and Anne Nuttall whilst on a walk in the Brecon Beacons and informed them of his find. A few weeks later a friend gave me a copy of an article by the Nuttalls in *Ramblers* magazine; they had visited this hill and confirmed its authenticity. Later in the year I bumped into Dewi around the Tarennydd, I told him about the article, we swopped addresses and I sent him a copy. Afterwards I wondered if any other new hill was waiting to be found. After all, using a minimum 15m criterion means that any continuous contour ring at or above 610 metres, would have a chance of qualifying for John and Anne's List and an awful lot of these existed amongst the Welsh hills. It also meant investigating many new parts of the country, places I would not have visited if it wasn't for this rather unusual and esoteric niche aspect of hill walking.

But where on Earth to begin; firstly some kind of measuring implement was needed. I soon found an old walking stick and a spirit level; I then scrutinised various Welsh maps for any continuous contour rings at or above 610m. Now with a rudimentary measuring staff and a detailed list of hilly bumps I could start the interesting process of trying to find another new Nuttall.

Dewi already had two prospective new Nuttalls in mind, Craiglwyn in the Carneddau, which he thought must be a definite entry, and Castell y Gwynt in the Glyderau. For my part I thought a rise on the north-western ridge of Carnedd Dafydd worth investigating. Slowly I started working my way through my "bumps to measure" list; thankfully few if any people were present on the hills as I rather self-consciously arrived at the designated col. Quickly the spirit level would be attached to the staff and readings taken; the process was repeated until the summit of the hilly bump was reached.

By this stage Dewi had informed me that John and Anne Nuttall had visited Craiglwyn and confirmed its entry in to their Welsh list. Spurred on by this Dewi then checked the rise on the north-western ridge of Carnedd Dafydd and reported that he had measured the drop of Foel Meirch to be over 15m, which John and Anne later confirmed. With these three additions, I thought the likelihood of other new Nuttalls was now more a probability than a possibility.

More bumpy bits were measured, and surprisingly it seemed a plethora of new Nuttalls was cropping up, but realising fewer vertical height measures would give greater accuracy and with my present staff only allowing an individual height measure of 0.75m, could my present method be trusted? I suspected not, so my quickly found walking stick was abandoned in favour of a purpose-built measuring staff that could be split into four via three brass screw fittings, thus enabling it to be carried inside a rucksack. The staff was manufactured with drilled holes at various height levels for attaching spirit levels. Now with this staff and a small post level, which I used for vertical alignment, I could have better confidence in my future results.

The survey method pioneered by Dewi relied upon a spirit level being attached to a staff at a designated height level, then by placing the bottom of the staff at the critical point of the col and horizontally sighting along the spirit level to a point such as a rock, then repeating the process from the said rock to another point, and so on, until the summit of the hill was reached, the drop value from col to summit would be obtained.

Soon two other hills became of particular interest, Waun Garnedd y Filiast in the Arenig and a fine shaped small top on the northern spur of Moelwyn Mawr. The former proved problematic with various visits paid to its moorland top, whilst the latter was only noticed whilst descending Moelwyn Mawr as it had been missed whilst compiling my 'bumps to survey' list. In time both hills would be accepted into John and Anne's list of 2,000ft mountains, and others would follow such as Waun Camddwr in the Aran and the hill listed as Waun Lefrith in the Mynydd Du range in south Wales.

Over a period of sixteen months I surveyed 164 separate bumpy bits for prospective Nuttall inclusion, and all close contenders were double-checked, the combined effort with Dewi resulted in seven new hills entering the Nuttalls' Welsh List.

The drop value of these seven new hills used a method now referred to as a basic levelling survey, but only one had been measured using a surveyor's level and staff.

This latter method produces highly accurate results and the hill surveyed using this method was the problematic moorland top of Waun Garnedd y Filiast. This hill had been surveyed using the basic levelling method on a number of occasions resulting in a measurement just exceeding 15m of drop. However it had then been visited by John and Anne Nuttall who had measured it as having less than 15m of drop. The resulting line survey was conducted by Harold Morris with Dewi, John Williams and myself in attendance to help with proceedings. The conclusion from the line survey of Waun Garnedd y Filiast was that its drop exceeded 15m and this was duly reported to John and Anne who then included it in their list.

After establishing these new hills for John and Anne's list my basic levelling surveys continued, and my attention was now drawn to the Deweys,[2] Y Pedwarau[3] and the Welsh 500m P15 tops, with in excess of 420 Welsh hills eventually being surveyed using this method. However I had only been present during one accurate line survey and my interest in this form of surveying was about to enter a new sphere when Anne Nuttall contacted me and asked if I could check the drop of a hill in the Y Berwyn range. Anne had been contacted by two people who had surveyed this Nuttall as having less than the required 15m of drop. They had used a surveyor's level and staff to survey the hill and their names were John Barnard and Graham Jackson.

The G and the J of Jackson and Barnard

Graham Jackson and John Barnard have been friends for many years, and both have grounding in the scientific world through their education and respective careers. Importantly, each has vast experience of the British hills having compleated the Munros, Corbetts, Grahams and the 2,000ft mountains of England and Wales. This combination of a scientific grounding and decades of hill walking gave an almost unique amalgam of

---

2   Deweys: English, Welsh and Manx hills at and above 500m and below 609.6m (2,000ft) in height with a minimum drop of 30m.

3   Y Pedwarau: Welsh hills at and above 400m and below 500m in height with a minimum drop of 30m.

interest in upland features and topographical science. This amalgam when combined with the person pottering around the Welsh hills with a basic measuring staff would revolutionise hill listings.

I duly surveyed the hill in the Y Berwyn and reported back to Anne Nuttall that it did not have the required 15m of drop for continued inclusion in their list. Anne then kindly forwarded Graham's contact details and within a couple of days Graham, John and I arranged to meet for a survey on another prospective Nuttall that I had surveyed as having over 15m of drop but which John and Anne had surveyed as having under.

The subsequent meeting and survey started a friendship and surveying team that was to last the next nine years which resulted in a revolution of hill status categorisation, as the three of us had enthusiasm and hill and science knowledge to push forward with an ambitious programme that quickly caught the eye of the mainstream media.

Within 16 months of meeting we organised a press conference to announce the result of a hill that had been surveyed in conjunction with Leica Geosystems. The name of the hill is Mynydd Graig Goch and the survey method used was that of Differential GPS which gives the height of any hill to an accurate level within 2-5cm and better dependent upon the time allocated for data collection.

The news that Mynydd Graig Goch was over 609.6m (2,000ft) in height, which is considered by many as the minimum height for a hill to be classified as a Welsh mountain was reported in a number of media outlets including national radio, television and tabloid and broadsheet newspapers. To list these would increase the length of this article substantially, but one example of the news coverage may sum up what had just happened, and that was when I sat down in the evening after the press conference to watch the 10:00pm ITN news and staring back at me on the TV screen was a photograph I had taken of the survey equipment in situ at the summit of the hill.

There was a number of advantages in organising a press conference to announce the survey result of Mynydd Graig Goch, one being to invite a representative of The Munro Society (TMS) to attend. TMS had previously pioneered the use of Differential GPS equipment to accurately survey the height of two hills in Scotland for possible Munro status when they approached CMCR Ltd to conduct each survey. The resulting heights of Beinn Dearg in Torridon and the Ganu Mor of Foinaven were announced at a press conference and received much attention. We were now doing likewise in Wales and a representative of TMS at our press conference enabled a fledgling working relationship to be established resulting in the newly named team of G&J Surveys being commissioned to take over the TMS Heightings project.

The Heightings

The Heightings project proved a unique opportunity to be a part of a team that would establish the status of hills close to the 3,000ft threshold within what many consider to be the most important hill list ever compiled to a selection of hills in Britain, i.e. *Munro's Tables*.

There are now in excess of 6,200 known compleaters of the Munros with probably three times this number slowly working their way through the list. For the hill bagging world the surveys we were about to undertake would prove historical.

Over the next five years we surveyed a number of hills for the Heightings project, resulting in Sgùrr nan Ceannaichean and Beinn a' Chlaidheimh being reclassified from Munro to Corbett status by the Scottish Mountaineering Club (SMC). A further survey of Knight's Peak was organised by us in conjunction with the SMC and involvement by TMS, resulting in its deletion from the Munro Tops.

These and other surveys in the Heightings project have given me an immense sense of fulfilment, both on a personal level and also from a team point of view, and I hope that the above portrays a sense of what the hills have given to me and the pleasure they have formed in my life. I also hope that in what follows, to give a sense of scale to the landscape in which the surveys for the Heightings project took place and the appreciation I have found from encountering the higher hills of Scotland.

Land of Mountain Giants – The Fisherfield Surveys

In the north-west of Scotland, bounded by an expanse of infinite sea, lies an alluring but remote land. Described by many as the last true wilderness in Britain, it is bordered to the north by the pinnacled defences of An Teallach, and to the south by the most remote of Munros. This is the land of the Fisherfield Forest, where long mountain days are required to visit any of its summits; it is a unique land of mountain giants.

The Fionn Loch looking east into Fisherfield (Iain A. Robertson)

It was our task to survey accurately three of these remote and inviting mountain giants. Would GPS technology show them not to be as high as once thought, with these surveys being a part of The Munro Society's ongoing Heighting project?

Our first objective was Beinn a' Chlaidheimh, a sandstone giant with a map height of 916m (3,005ft) that overlooks the wildly situated mountain bothy of Shenavall. We set off with members of TMS from Corrie Hallie on the 'Destitution Road', gaining height on a good track until the land of the Fisherfield Forest opened up before us. Few landscapes in the whole of Britain can compare! With a radiant blue sky, glistening lochs and mountain tops free of cloud, all our party had to do was carry the 12kg of surveying equipment up to the summit, which comprises three separate tops of nearly equal height. Using a survey-grade optical level and staff, we soon determined that the most southerly of these is the highest. To determine accurate summit height, we used a Leica-Geosystems 530 GPS. This equipment operates in a similar way to a car's SatNav or a small hand-held GPS unit, although its accuracy is far superior to these.

We set the equipment up on the mountain's highest point and proceeded to collect three hours of data which would be submitted to Ordnance Survey for computation of the accurate height. During this time we could now rest and fully appreciate the beauty of our surroundings. Across Gleann na Muice the next surveying objective of Beinn Dearg Mòr rose island-like from out of the valley depths, with occasional cloud shadows silently moving across its steep eastern face. Towards the south-west, the rounded summit of our third surveying objective, Ruadh Stac Mòr, was a wilderness away. Both hills would demand long days with their summits proving hard to reach.

With three hours of data collected, we packed the equipment away and descended back to the valley below and the Abhainn Loch an Nid river crossing. Thankfully this proved relatively easy with no problems encountered, something that is not always the case with the river crossings within the Fisherfield area. However, with almost 900ft of re-ascent required to get back to Corrie Hallie, the remoteness of the Fisherfield Forest was now appreciated more by the weariness of body rather than the alertness of one's mind and its awareness of remote landscape in all its beauty. The day proved long with the last of the eight-strong party arriving back at the awaiting cars after 12½ hours on the hill.

A well-earned recovery day at Sàil Mhòr Hostel followed. On the second walk from Corrie Hallie into Fisherfield along with members of The Munro Society we were joined by the expedition's sponsor, Lord Haworth of Fisherfield, the first member of the Upper House to become a Munroist. The weather proved less favourable than on our first outing with persistent rain during our inward and outward route to and from Shenavall, with intermittent spots of rain accompanying us for much of the rest of the day. With, in all, four river crossings to overcome, we were again thankful that these proved relatively easy, but ahead, cloud capped, lay our next surveying objective, Beinn Dearg Mòr. With a map height of 910m (2,985½ft) this hill is one of the highest, and regarded as one of the best of the Corbetts, these being Scottish mountains at and above 2,500ft and below 3,000ft in height with a minimum 500ft of rise on all sides. Its reputation is one well deserved, with any approach being steep and unrelenting, leading to narrow ridges and spectacular buttresses. We were free of cloud whilst surveying for the summit position and once set up the equipment proceeded to gather two hours of data. Once the survey was complete the equipment was packed away and we started our descent. The walk out proved equally as gruelling as our inward journey, and some members of our twelve-strong party experienced an eighteen-hour day on the hill!

On the following rest day, we visited the factor at the Letterewe Estate, who kindly gave us permission to leave cars above Poolewe at Kernsary. Although this saved us six miles of walking, the third day's expedition still proved a long one with 22

Rainbow from Ruadh Stac Mòr (Glen Breaden)

miles covered in all. The approach towards Ruadh Stac Mòr and its map listed 918m (3,011¾ft) trig pillar proved almost alpine-like, with long valleys leading toward the hills as we quickly gained ground on good paths. Mountain architecture of the finest order seemed to enfold us, enticing our onward investigation. The weather forecast predicted heavy, prolonged, localised showers with the possibility of thunder and lightning. Thankfully, only one shower materialised and this approached us whilst we were on the summit. On clearing westward it left a magical view below us of a double rainbow, which stayed with us for many minutes as clearing skies once more brought gentle hued colours to the mountain landscape. This area really is quite special! With two hours of data collected we packed the equipment away and descended out of the Fisherfield Forest, arriving back at the awaiting cars after another long mountain day.

Sometimes figures can highlight the task completed and those for our three surveying days came to an approximate 55 miles walked with 14,600ft of ascent and totalling over 41 hours on the hills.

Although the experience of being in this remote mountain environment was one never to be forgotten, ultimately the reason for being there was the measurement of these mountains' heights. Would any of these three mountain giants alter in their listed status? It was no surprise that our surveyed summit height of 918.69m is in accordance with the 918.67m flush bracket height adjoined to Ruadh Stac Mòr's triangulation pillar. More surprising is the result of Beinn Dearg Mòr whose 910m map height was reduced due to our 906.39m survey result. Both of these hills retain their respective Munro and Corbett status. But what about the sandstone giant of Beinn a' Chlaidheimh? Would having a map height of 916m (3,005ft) prove it vulnerable to reclassification? The answer to this question awaited data post-processing. Because of its importance, this result, along with that of Beinn Dearg Mòr was sent to Mark Greaves, the Ordnance Survey's Geodetic Analyst who independently processed each result. The outcome was that Beinn a' Chlaidheimh's accurately surveyed summit height was calculated to be 914.03m (2,998ft 9 inches) which is below that of the 914.4m (3,000ft) benchmark height. Therefore, upon SMC verification, Beinn a' Chlaidheimh was no longer listed as a Munro and was reclassified to Corbett status. However, although the Munros are now reduced to 282 separate Mountains, the Corbetts increase in total to 221 mountains. And although Beinn a' Chlaidheimh can no longer boast Munro status, it is still a mountain giant, positioned in a vast land of remote peaks, remaining the same in all but known height and classification.

The Skye Cuillin – Britain's Most Difficult Mountain Surveys

The Black Cuillin Mountains of Skye are renowned in Britain for having a unique architecture. With vertical black gabbro monoliths rising out of high corries and sides of mountains cut sheer as they plunge to rock strewn boulder fields, they form the most challenging mountain environment anywhere in Britain. Scrambling up to their summits is like reaching the top of the world to look over the edge into hostile oblivion. This is a land of unworldliness where eagles can soar, and narrow complicated ridges requiring a mountaineer's knowledge and skill predominate.

It was into this land of vertical rock that we ventured to survey two of the most technically difficult Munro Tops. This venture had been planned for many months but we had considered its difficulties and challenges for a number of years. Mountain surveying is not new to us as we had surveyed over 150 summits in the previous seven years. These comprise a variety of tops, from ploughed fields in Wiltshire to 1,000m high mountains in Snowdonia, but none compared with the task we now set ourselves, as the Black Cuillin is like nothing else in Britain.

The two Munro Tops we aimed to survey were Knight's Peak and the Bhàsteir Tooth. Both are in the north of the Black Cuillin of Skye. Knight's Peak is the fourth pinnacle on Pinnacle Ridge that leads in a south-westerly direction up to the summit of Sgùrr nan Gillean. The Bhàsteir Tooth is a shard of rock attached precariously on the western face of Am Bàsteir. Both require technical climbing to attain their summits and the exposure is not conducive to the carrying of awkward and heavy loads. Consequently, the surveys required much planning and attention to detail.

As Munro Tops, Knight's Peak and the Bhàsteir Tooth have entries in *Munros Tables*. The list consists of Separate Mountains, eponymously known as Munros, and Subsidiary Tops, now known as Munro Tops. It is arguably the most popular list of mountains in Britain. As Knight's Peak had a map height of 915m (3,002ft) and the Bhàsteir Tooth is given a height of 916m (3,005ft), each summit was close to the threshold qualifying height of 914.40m (3,000.0ft). And as these map heights have a margin of uncertainty of +/-3m we wanted to obtain an accurate and definitive height for each using the latest GPS technology.

The participants for this most difficult of mountain surveys gathered at Portnalong on the Isle of Skye in early September 2013. The team comprised the surveyors John Barnard,

The gear in place on Knight's Peak (©Myrddyn Phillips)

Graham Jackson and Myrddyn Phillips from G&J Surveys and Alan Dawson, who was invited to survey the second summit of Knight's Peak. Representing the Scottish Mountaineering Club (SMC) were Andy Nisbet, a past President of the organisation and one of the best Scottish winter climbers the country has ever produced, and Noel Williams, the author of the SMC guide, *Skye Scrambles*. There were also present members of The Munro Society (TMS), with the survey of the Bhàsteir Tooth having been chosen by the latter organisation. All we now required was favourable weather, and in particular, no wind and adequate visibility.

The 11th of September dawned wet and dank but with a limited time frame of only five days on Skye and a forecast for improvement, we took our opportunity to venture into and up to this vertical world of rock.

Following the path that starts near the Sligachan Hotel, we made good progress beside the waterfalls and clear green pools of Allt Dearg Beag. Height was gained as first Coire Riabhach and then the high corrie at the eastern base of Pinnacle Ridge was reached. Views of our objective were shielded as mist was low in the upper corrie and this gave an eerie ambiance to our surroundings, as buttressed rock was hidden from view with only an occasional glimpse of shrouded grey verticality.

We took a grassy runnel that led up to the edge of the lower rock of Pinnacle Ridge and side stepped the lower rock-strewn gulley which we joined higher up and which gave access to the world of plunging drops and hair-raising traverses.

The upper gully is graded as a difficult climb and this is where the party donned hard protective helmets and climbing harnesses before Andy Nisbet assisted our ascents from above. Soon the airy perch of the bealach between Knight's Peak and Sgùrr nan Gillean was reached and one by one we made our delicate way traversing around the bulk of the mountain. All necessary surveying equipment was being carried by the party with this consisting of an automatic level and staff, tripod, Leica GS15 GNSS receiver, pole and a small tripod. Heavy rucksacks dictated a slow ascent from the lower traverse up a rock band to another higher traverse until a rocky rib led up to the highest rocks of Knight's Peak. All around us was a shielding cover of mist with vertical drops plunging in all directions into the grey murk. The area of the summit consists of two tops; we used a small hand-held Abney level to sight from one to the other as it proved impossible and would be highly dangerous to attempt to set up a surveyor's level in such a restricted environment. Our preliminary assessment with the Abney level made the northern summit about 0.1m higher. Soon our GS15 was set up on the small tripod and aligned with the high point of the northern summit, whilst Alan Dawson set up his Leica RX1250 on the very highest point of the southern summit. A two-hour vigil now started as Ordnance Survey requires a minimum two-hour data set for verification of the result.

Occasional glimpses of the sun were spotted as the grey massed bulk of the towering northern flank of Sgùrr nan Gillean edged its silhouetted profile into view and then was hidden as the mist once again swallowed all before it. However, the power of the sun was winning the battle and an unforgettable last half hour of data collection ensued, as slowly the mist lowered and blue sky appeared to reveal pinnacled summits jutting through the sea of whiteness below. Sgùrr nan Gillean shot up in front of us and then we were treated to a Brocken spectre; the dramatic beauty of such surroundings was

Am Bàsteir in sight (©Myrddyn Phillips)

On the approach to the Bhàsteir Tooth (©Myrddyn Phillips)

now harshly on show. The sheer vertical world of our precarious position was laid before us, as the precipitous drops hidden by mist that were previously known to be there, were now all too clearly shown as the sides of Knight's Peak sped downward in an uncompromising jumble of rock.

With the two-hour vigil now over and the data stored, we packed all the equipment away and with Andy's expert guidance we reversed the upward route down toward the bealach and the awaiting gully. Overcoming this last barrier, we had a slow walk back to the road in the valley below. We'd been out on the hill for ten hours and had completed the most difficult mountain survey we had ever attempted and probably the most difficult mountain survey ever completed in Britain. All that was now required was the survey of the Bhàsteir Tooth.

Two days later on the 13th September we were out relatively early and were met by Noel Williams, who along with Andy Nisbet were to form an integral part of the success of the next survey. The Munro Society had arranged this survey and was represented on the day by Colin Walter and Alan Brook. Both are highly skilled in mountain craft with years of mountain and caving experience respectively.

This second survey was different from the first as the peaks of the Cuillin were on show as sun shone out of the September sky. Although showers were forecast, the outlook for the day was good. We again made our way up beside Allt Dearg Beag and crossed on to its eastern side and followed the land up to the base of Pinnacle Ridge. Away to our south-east the shapely summit of Marsco rose out of the valley, its sides shining, blue tinged in the early morning sun, with the sublime rugged beauty of Blà Bheinn's

The surveyors on the Bhàsteir Tooth (©Myrddyn Phillips)

serrated summit profile being etched in the memory.

From here a path across scree followed the base of the western flank of Pinnacle Ridge. Above us rose Knight's Peak, a huge mass of rock that punctuated the higher realm of sky. Soon the morning's welcome sunshine was overtaken with thickening grey murk that descended upon the castellated tops and took us in its grasp as drops of rain fell from above. In time, the scree path led to the Bealach a' Bhàsteir and with the shower now ended the Cuillin dispensed a magical show of highlighted colour as wisps of mist slowly threaded through rocky spires. Ahead was Am Bàsteir. The way to this Munro's summit was on a narrowing ridge and its well-known 'Bad Step' was negotiated with the aid of a rope set up by Noel and Andy. Reaching its summit was truly like walking to the top of the world and looking over its edge.

Beyond the summit the party took up a stance on a small flat area of ground overlooking a steep gully. One by one we were belayed over the edge to reach the narrow confines of the gap between Am Bàsteir and its Tooth. The top of The Tooth was our surveying objective and this consisted of a large boulder that somehow had become balanced firmly in place on the monolith that is The Tooth. Beside it was a small cairn. The survey equipment was soon in place and aligned for its two-hour data collection. During this time, the day's second shower appeared and accentuated the slipperiness of the basalt rock of which the Tooth is made. Once the data had been gathered and the equipment packed away, we slithered down the Tooth and made an unceremonious arrival at the gap between it and Am Bàsteir. From here we slid through a hole and a small cave to a chamber where Noel had set up an abseil point from which we were belayed down the 80ft of vertical rock that forms King's Cave Chimney to a steep scree slope below.

Feeling well pleased with the success of the survey a weary trudge led back to the awaiting cars at Sligachan in the valley below.

All that remained was to post-process the data and have the result verified by Ordnance Survey. The large monolith that forms the vertical world of the Bhàsteir Tooth has a height of 917.15m (3,009ft 2 inches), a rise of 1m above its current map height. But what about that most difficult of mountain surveys, the one to the vertical world of the hair-raising traverses of Knight's Peak? With a height of 914.25m (2,999ft 6 inches) it just failed to retain its Munro Top status by an approximate 6½ inches!

The mountains of the Skye Black Cuillin are there for the adventurous in spirit and the Bhàsteir Tooth will remain a Munro Top, albeit 1m higher than previously thought. But now that fourth pinnacle, the one that was first ascended in 1873 by W. Knight and a local guide named MacPherson, will no longer be listed as a Munro Top. Although this hallowed status has been taken away, its presence as one of the most challenging of mountains to ascend for the non-climber remains intact and will be forevermore, whatever the status now awarded it.

I would like to express my thanks to Iain Robertson for instigating The Heightings project as it proved a wonderful experience to be a part of, one that will last with me for many years to come. My thanks are also given to John and Graham as what we shared will bring a smile to my face for years to come.

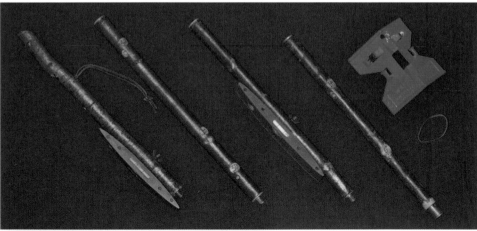

Above: Third measuring staff
(© Myrddyn Phillips)

Left: Detail of third measuring staff
(© Myrddyn Phillips)

Chapter 10

Lists Beyond the Munros

Graham Jackson and Alan Dawson

Following the publication in 1891 of Munro's list of the Scottish 3,000ft mountains, one might have expected an explosion of enthusiasm from those interested in the British mountains, which would result in similar lists being published for all areas of Britain. In the event there was silence for nearly two decades. Were would-be authors put off after coming to terms with the enormity of Munro's achievement? We will never know.

The next author to break the silence has a very familiar name – John Rooke Corbett. He was a district valuer based in Bristol and, of course, is well known for his list of 2,500ft hills of Scotland. However, his first foray into compiling hill lists was his publication of the Twenty-Fives in 1911.[1] This was a list of the mountains over 2,500ft in England and Wales. The original list contained well over 100 hills and was published in the Rucksack Club journal. Such was its popularity with members that it was revised at least three times over the following two decades, by Corbett himself and also once by Edward Moss.

Although Corbett's lists covered the whole of Britain, his lists for England and Wales were supplemented and later superseded by other lists, so that his name became associated only with his list of Scottish hills. For several decades it became common practice for Scotland to be treated separately, while England and Wales were treated as a single entity for hill listing purposes. The structure of this chapter reflects that distinction. However, there was one list compiler who covered all of the British Isles but whose name – William Docharty – is not well known, even in hill walking circles. There are reasons for this. His three books, issued from 1954 to 1962, were printed privately and in limited numbers, so they received little publicity. They were beautifully produced and well illustrated, but their structure and titles were immensely confusing. Furthermore, his lists had no clear definition, other than excluding hills already listed by Munro or Corbett. One consequence was that Docharty's work was largely ignored by the Scottish Mountaineering Club, even though he was an active club member. Perhaps this was understandable, given that there was no single clear list or definition, or perhaps hills under 2,500 feet high in Scotland were regarded as hardly worth bothering with when there were so many hills over that height.[2]

It was another forty years before comprehensive lists of lower hills in Scotland were published, but substantial hill listing work was going on south of the border.

England and Wales

The first list of 2,000ft hills of England was published by W T Elmslie in 1933. Some of the criteria used for compiling the list were idiosyncratic when compared with the criteria used by hill list compilers today. For example, any height above 2,000ft marked

---

1   See *Corbett and the English and Welsh 2,500ft Peaks*, Irvine Butterfield, in *TMS Journal No.4*, 2016.
2   See *The Life and Work of William McKnight Docharty*, Robin Campbell, in *TMS Journal No.4*, 2016.

with a cairn on the map was included, as was any spot height above 2,000ft. These criteria led to Red Tarn and two passes being included along with an indeterminate number of cairns not actually on summits. These were then subtracted to give a final total between 290 and 320 summits. A regional list followed just four years later, in 1937, when F H F Simpson published a list of hills of 2,000ft and over for the Lake District, based on single ring contours from the Ordnance Survey one-inch map. For the first time the concept of drop (or re-ascent or prominence, as it is also known) was being considered as a criterion, although this would probably not have been appreciated at the time. (An earlier regional list by Carr and Lister did refer to 100ft of drop as a criterion, but this was not applied rigorously, and there was an earlier reference to the use of single ring contours in 1929 by Moss, although this was a revision of the Twenty-Fives and not a new list). Just two years later in 1939 Edward Moss applied the same criteria and extended the list to cover all of England, and in 1940, Wales. Over the next two decades Moss's list was revised and updated and was the standard list used by hill walkers during that period.

The next major advance came in 1973 when George Bridge published his book of *The Mountains of England and Wales*. There were 408 summits in Bridge's list and these were divided into separate mountains and tops, following the lead set by Hugh Munro's list of Scottish 3,000ft mountains published eight decades earlier. Bridge used a 50ft drop criterion for defining his summits (the one-inch map gave contours at 50ft intervals) and 2,000ft for minimum height. He acknowledged the ideas and work of previous authors and his book became the standard reference for hill walkers over the next sixteen years. Although the book is no longer in print, for those interested in seeing Bridge's list, it is given on the websites of the Database of British and Irish Hills (www.hills-database.co.uk and www.hill-bagging.co.uk).

In 1986 Chris Buxton and Gwyn Lewis published *The Mountain Summits of England and Wales*. In the intervening years Ordnance Survey had published the Second Series 1:50,000 and 1:25,000 maps which gave hill-list compilers a clearer and more accurate appreciation of upland topography. The criteria used by Buxton and Lewis, in compiling their list, were that the hill had to be 2,000ft or over in height and have a 'minimum rise of 10m above the immediate surrounding area'. In effect this meant that there had to be two 10m ring contours between the summit and its col. Additionally, it was appreciated that some distinct hills might have two or more points of similar height on an undulating plateau, in which case only the highest point was taken: the example given was Kinder Scout. The list comprised 423 hills split into eleven regions which included the Isle of Man. Buxton and Lewis's list is no longer in print, but this is also given on the websites of the Database of British and Irish Hills.

Despite the advances made by Buxton and Lewis and their use of the latest maps, Bridge's work was still used by many hill-goers. Perhaps people were becoming confused by the wealth of information and books now available to those interested in the outdoors and in hills in particular. For example, W A Poucher published *The Lakeland Peaks* in 1960 and this was in its eighth edition by 1981, such was its popularity. This was not a list, but a guide, and was one of many. In addition other non-criterion based lists were now being published, of which more will be described later in this chapter.

Also during the 1980s a series of guides was written by Terry Marsh. These were: *The Mountains of Wales, The Lake Mountains: One, The Lake Mountains: Two* and *The Pennine Mountains*. While these were guides giving a wealth of detail on routes, along with distances and ascent for each walk, each book also listed, in order of altitude, the hills contained in each volume. These were split into two lists, one for hills over 600m and with 30m or more of drop and a second list for hills over 600m, but with less than 30m of drop (no minimum drop criterion was given for this list). The volumes were also illustrated with photographs taken by the author.

So by the closing years of the 1980s authors of hill lists for England and Wales were beginning to use criteria that we are familiar with today. 2,000ft was still the criterion of choice for height, although Terry Marsh had broken with that tradition and used the metric criterion of 600m and drop was now also used with authors adopting 50ft (just over 15m) or 30m in the case of Marsh. The Ordnance Survey 1:50,000 and 1:25,000 Second Series maps were now the source of information. Where would the next breakthrough arise?

Nuttalls

In 1989 the first of two volumes by John and Anne Nuttall entitled *The Mountains of England and Wales Volume 1: Wales* was published. This was followed a year later by *Volume 2: England*. The guides are illustrated by pen and ink drawings and maps, while the route descriptions contain much background information as well as personal accounts of days in the mountains.

These volumes were the result of painstaking research on the part of the authors. Their starting definition of a mountain was that it had to be 2,000ft or over and have a drop of 50ft or more. However, since metric maps were now in use this was refined to 610m (2,000ft to the nearest metre, but more accurately 609.6m) for height and 15m for drop. So this followed on naturally from the work of Bridge and Buxton & Lewis whose lists were based on 2,000ft as a minimum height and 50ft for drop, but now the metric equivalents were accepted. The latest Second Series Ordnance Survey maps were used at 1:50,000 and 1:25,000 scales and where necessary the 1:10,000 maps were also consulted.

But the research went further than this because the authors drew up a shortlist of tops where drop could not be clearly defined from maps. Scores of candidates were visited and surveyed and many discoveries were made on their walks. Some could be easily dismissed (50ft is quite a big rise!) but many had to be surveyed in order to determine their respective drops. The technique used a spirit level and was the result of a recommendation by Ordnance Survey. Standing at a col one person sights a horizontal line with the spirit level and identifies a feature on the hill level with their position. The other person then climbs to that position. Once the feet of that person align with the spirit level they stop and the surveyor then moves to that position also. This procedure is then repeated until the top of the hill is reached. The drop is then the height of the level above the ground for each placement multiplied by the number of placements plus any fractional height for the final leg. While simple and employing only simple equipment, the technique is remarkably good. G&J Surveys has compared several such surveys and found that for drops of around 15m on steep ground the accuracy is of the order of 0.5m. Where the distance between col and summit is large and therefore the gradient shallow, then the potential error for 15m of drop may approach 2m. Nevertheless, this is considerably better than estimating drop from a map.

The publication of these volumes inspired others to search for new Nuttalls (as the hills in the guides became known) and between 1991 and 2009 ten new tops were added and one deleted. Hill walkers soon took the hills described in these volumes to be the definitive list of 2,000ft hills, thus displacing Bridge's list as the definitive work. However, it should be noted that the authors produced a guide to climbing the hills rather than setting out to produce just a list. Guide books being turned into lists by the hill walking community is a recurring theme. Since then there have been further changes to the guides, most of these brought about using the same GNSS technology that has been used for the Munros and described in this book. The Nuttalls' List is still the definitive list for the 2,000ft hills with 15m minimum drop. The current totals stand at 189 tops in Wales and 256 tops in England giving a grand total of 445 separate tops.

Deweys

In 1995 Michael Dewey published a list of hills in England and Wales of 500m and over in height with a minimum drop of 30m. This work, therefore, included the hills from the Nuttalls' List that had 30m or more of drop and lowered the height criterion to encompass hills down to 500m. The list did not immediately gain popularity, but very soon hill walkers saw merit in those hills below 609.6m (2,000ft) in height and over the intervening years the Deweys were accepted to be hills of 500m or over in height, but less than 609.6m in height with a minimum drop of 30m. There were originally 373 Deweys, a total that was increased to over 440 by several people, but principally by David Purchase, Rob Woodall, Clem Clements and Myrddyn Phillips. Over the last ten years or so surveys carried out mainly with level and staff and/or survey-grade GNSS receivers have reduced the total to the current number of 426. The Deweys List in its modern form has gathered an increasing number of devotees but, to date, the number of people known to have climbed them only stands at a dozen or so.

Hewitts

In 1997 the Hewitts were introduced, an acronym for Hills in England, Wales and Ireland over 2,000ft. Three separate booklets were produced in a series of *TACit Tables*, one for Wales, one for England (both by Alan Dawson) and one for Ireland (by E D Clements). The key feature was to identify and include hills with at least 30m drop, thereby excluding many of the hills in the Nuttalls' List.

Scotland

For most of the twentieth century, the primary authority for hill lists in Scotland was the book of *Munro's Tables and Other Tables of Lesser Heights*, published periodically by the Scottish Mountaineering Club. Several editions of this publication included Corbett's list of Scottish hills from 2,500 to 2,999 feet and also a list of hills in southern Scotland, compiled by Percy Donald. It was not until 1997 that the book of *Munro's Tables* included a list of hills from 2,000 to 2,500ft high, which by that time had become known as the Grahams. The list was simple to understand but had a complex history.

Docharty, Yeaman and Torbet

The three books by William Docharty, published from 1954-1962, included almost all the hills now known as Grahams, but these were intermingled within a much larger set of hills. Docharty did classify hills into separate mountains and subsidiary tops, following the pattern set by Munro, but there was no clear definition of either. Docharty's works can therefore be regarded as hugely impressive personal lists, more a record of hills he had climbed than a systematic attempt at a comprehensive listing.

Several other people are known to have compiled their own lists of Scottish hills from 2,000 to 2,500ft high, but none was published or well known. It was not until 1989 that the first extensive listing of Scottish hills under 2,500ft high was published, in *Handbook of the Scottish Hills*, by E J Yeaman. This work has now been superseded by more accurate and comprehensive lists, described later, but it represented an important stage in covering Scottish hills under 2,500ft high. At the time most of these hills were very little known. Yeaman's use of 100m drop or 5km distance as qualifying criteria were applied rather vaguely but nonetheless marked an important step in the evolution of the list now known as Humps.

Hills with at least 150m drop were included but not identified in Yeaman's book, but soon afterwards, in 1992, these were published in *The Relative Hills of Britain*, by Alan Dawson. The 222 Scottish hills from 2,000 to 2,500ft high were included but not listed separately and were to some extent lost within a larger work, as in the books by Docharty and Yeaman. A mere half a page was allocated to describing the *Lesser Corbetts*, as Dawson referred to them, abbreviated to *Elsies*. However, a significant difference from Docharty's works was that the list of Elsies had a clear definition and could be easily extracted from the larger set.

Six months after Dawson's book was published, The Great Outdoors magazine published a list of 244 hills in the Scottish Highlands from 2,000 to 2,500ft high, compiled by Fiona Torbet and referred to as Grahams (Torbet's maiden name). This had an extensive overlap with the 222 Elsies, but excluded southern Scotland, omitted twelve qualifying hills and included 56 hills not listed by Dawson as they had less than 150m drop. Having waited until 1992 for such a list to appear, there were now two available within six months of each other. In order to avoid the confusion and inconvenience of two similar but different lists, Dawson and Torbet got together to produce a revised list of 224 Grahams. Dawson took advice from Torbet regarding some hill names and the height of Beinn Talaidh on Mull, but the resulting list was essentially the Scottish Elsies renamed as the Grahams, a more satisfactory name. Torbet issued her own revised listing shortly before her death in 1993, with some minor differences in hill names where the two authors had agreed to differ. In subsequent years, Dawson continued to maintain and update the list and to retain the name Grahams, to honour the verbal agreement made with Fiona Torbet and to help commemorate one of the few women to have compiled and published a list of hills.

The list of Grahams was offered to the Scottish Mountaineering Club Journal in December 1992 but rejected on the grounds that 'the last thing we need is a proliferation of lists'. It was first published as a separate work in 1995 in *The Grahams and the New Donalds*, by Alan Dawson, the first in the *TACit Tables* series. In 1997 the Grahams were adopted by the SMC, by agreement between Donald Bennet, SMC publications editor at the time, and Alan Dawson. The list of 224 Grahams published in the book of *Munro's Tables* in 1997 was accurate at the time and remained unchanged for 17 years, until GNSS surveying enabled more accurate heights of summits and cols to be established.

Murdos, Corbett Tops and Graham Tops

In 1995, Alan Dawson produced a booklet called *The Murdos*, covering 444 Scottish hills over 3,000 feet with 30 metres of relative height. This was an attempt to introduce greater precision into the list of higher Scottish hills. It has now been superseded by other lists and more accurate measurements, but it did highlight some notable omissions and inaccuracies in *Munro's Tables* (e.g. the height of Spidean Coire nan Clach on Beinn Eighe was 993m, not 972m). Seven new summits were included that had never been listed by Hugh Munro or subsequent editors of the Tables. All seven, plus one more, were added to the list of Munros and Tops published by the SMC in 1997.

The same formula used to define the Murdos was extended to hills from 2,500 to 2,999ft high in the publication in 1999 of *Corbett Tops and Corbetteers*, by Alan Dawson and Dave Hewitt. This covered 669 qualifying hills with at least 30 metres of relative height. The odd mix of units, with an imperial height threshold but a metric drop criterion, reflected the historical importance of imperial height bands and some rigidity of thought by the authors.

Dawson was reluctant to extend the concept of Murdos and Corbett Tops to hills below 2,500 feet as he thought that such a list would be inaccurate, difficult to compile and of little interest to hill walkers. However, with some inevitability a listing was duly published (*Graham Tops and Grahamists*), drawing on earlier work by E D Clements and James Gordon and using the most accurate map data available at the time (2004). Demand for this booklet was slight, confirming Dawson's original reservations. However he continued to attempt to improve the accuracy of the published data using GNSS technology.

Britain

Marilyns

In a well-known article published in 1933, entitled *Munros, Beards and the Weather*, John Dow observed that 'a business-like classification would have to take into account the following factors, of importance in the order named, (1) dip (2) distance and (3) difficulty'.

Subsequent editors of *Munro's Tables* resisted any such classification, but Dow's comments showed that the concept variously known as dip, drop, relative height, re-ascent, rise and prominence had been regarded as important for many years before it became systematically applied to hills of any height. *The Relative Hills of Britain*, by Alan Dawson, listed 1,542 hills of any height with at least 150m of relative height (the current total is 1,556). These hills were referred to as the Marilyns in a forlorn attempt to deter some hill walkers from taking themselves too seriously. Yeaman and Torbet had both attempted to incorporate Dow's second factor, distance, as well as relative height, but Dawson did not.

The list of Marilyns includes all the Corbetts, all the Grahams, and 202 of the hills in Munro's list. Almost half of the Marilyns are over 2,000ft high and so it is incorrect to regard them as primarily lower hills. The salient feature was the use of relative height as the sole criterion, so any hill over 150m high could be eligible for inclusion. Like Munro's list, the Marilyns were subject to several revisions after publication, so a set of Submarilyns was identified, with 140-149m drop, to help keen and prudent hill baggers to protect themselves from being caught out by future promotions.

By the end of 2017 over 340 people had climbed at least 600 Marilyns, making them eligible for the Marilyn Hall of Fame, and over 130 had climbed at least 1,000 Marilyns, but only ten people had managed to climb all 1,556. Some lower hills, notably the St Kilda sea stacks, proved to be far more difficult to reach and climb than any of the higher Scottish hills.

A Marilyn – Mullach an Eilein, Boreray, St Kilda (Derek Sime)

Humps

With the increasing popularity of the Marilyns, it was only a matter of time before the concept of hill lists based only on prominence or drop was exploited further. In fact a surprisingly long time elapsed because it was not until 2007 that the Humps were published, by Mark Jackson. The name derives from **Hu**ndred **M**etre **P**rominence, since the list was all hills in the UK, Isle of Man and Channel Islands with 100m or more of drop. The reason for the delay was probably in no small part due to the significant amount of work involved in identifying the large number of hills fulfilling this criterion although, of course, by definition the list also includes the Marilyns. Not surprisingly, since its publication there have been many changes to the list and the current total stands at 2,987 hills.[3] Of these 2,165 are in Scotland, 445 in England, 366 in Wales, 11 in the Isle of Man and 3 in the Channel Islands; this larger total of 2,990 is due to three hills lying on country borders. An e-book of the Humps was published by Mark Jackson in 2009.

So, over one hundred years after publication of the Munros, criterion-based hill lists had evolved into two major branches; lists such as the Nuttalls which had a minimum height criterion plus a drop criterion, and lists such as the Marilyns which had only a drop criterion. Were there any further niches that would-be authors could exploit? The answer is, of course, yes.

Simms

When the Ordnance Survey started to publish maps with spot heights in metres rather than feet in the 1970s, it made sense for hill list compilers and editors to use metric units. The Scottish Mountaineering Club led the way, with the 1974 edition of *Munro's Tables*, edited by J C Donaldson, listing heights in metres as well as feet. One consequence of the change was that the familiar and neat height bands of 3,000, 2,500 and 2,000ft became converted to 914.4, 762.0 and 609.6 metres. This meant that a hill shown on an OS map as 914m high might be over or under 3,000 feet, and one shown as 610m might be under 2,000ft.

It would have made sense for hill listers to adjust their height criteria to metric values, but Terry Marsh was the only one who did so. The series of TACit Tables retained the original height bands, as did works by the Nuttalls, Dewey and others. It was not until 2010 that Alan Dawson finally abandoned the imperial height bands and introduced the Simms, comprising all the British hills over 600m high with at least 30m of relative height. The aim was to unify and simplify existing lists (Murdos, Corbett Tops, Graham Tops, Hewitts), abandon unwieldy acronyms such as GTC (Graham Top of a Corbett), and apply the same criteria to Scotland as to England and Wales. The resulting list was huge, currently 2,528 hills, so it is not surprising that by the end of 2017 only two people had managed to climb them all, with eight others past the 2,000 mark. The Inaccessible Pinnacle is probably the hardest of these hills to climb, but there are several others that require hard scrambling or moderate rock climbing, such as Bidein Druim nan Ramh and Sgùrr na Uamha on Skye, and A' Chir and Torr Ceum na Caillich on Arran.

---

3   Hill list totals are as of May 2018.

The list of Simms is still being revised and updated, and so a definitive list of all of them has not yet been published. However, the inclusion of the Simms on the well-used Hill Bagging website has led to a slow increase in the popularity of the concept as well as the hills. However, many of the hills in the Monadhliath have fewer than ten recorded ascents. Most hill baggers still use feet to define their hill ambitions.

Tumps

Hill lists with only a drop criterion have also evolved further. In 2009 Mark Jackson published the Tumps (**T**hirty and **U**pward **M**etre **P**rominences) which comprise all the hills of Britain with 30m or more of drop and with no minimum height. As for the Humps, the list of Tumps incorporates several other hill lists such as Marilyns, Humps and Simms, and consequently the work of many others over the years has contributed directly or indirectly to this task. Mark Jackson completed three years of research of hills below 300 metres in height, which finally enabled the list to be compiled. The list of Tumps has, not surprisingly, been updated several times since its publication. The current total stands at close to 17,000. It perhaps sets the ultimate challenge for the hill walker. Many who have taken up this challenge set themselves achievable goals. For example, one such goal is climbing all those hills in a specific area, locality or county. This is fairly easy in local authorities such as Dundee and Glasgow, which each have four Tumps, but more of a challenge in Highland region, which has 4,229. No-one has yet climbed them all but two people are over half way there.

These examples are not the end of the story. For example, lists of hills between 400m and 499m with 30m or more of drop have been published for England (The Fours) and Wales (Y Pedwarau) by Myrddyn Phillips and Aled Williams. No doubt this will inspire others to reduce the height or drop criterion further and publish new lists. It remains to be seen how eager the walking community is for these new and, as yet, undefined challenges.

Dodds

The introduction of Simms and Tumps to cover the whole of Britain removed the anomaly of using mixed units, but introduced another one, as hills between 600 and 609.6 metres high were included in overlapping lists. A small group of tidy-minded hill enthusiasts attempted to resolve this anomaly by defining a unified list of hills from 500 to 599m high with 30m drop. These were to be the Dodds, the next band down from the Simms. There are currently 1,339 hills in this category and, almost incredibly, one person (Ken Whyte) has climbed all but three of the 948 in Scotland. One of the remaining three is the Old Man of Storr on Skye, which is way beyond the abilities and ambitions of almost all hill baggers. It is probably not the hardest Tump, as there are some extremely difficult sea stacks, such as Stac Biorach in St Kilda, but it does make it unlikely that anyone will climb all the Dodds in the near future. However, that has not deterred keen hill baggers from collecting as many as they can before their legs give out or they find something better to do.

Local lists

Lake District

So far in this chapter we have followed the development, from 1891 to the present day, of hill lists based on some criterion, usually height and or drop. Indeed the majority of hill lists today follow this protocol. There is, however, another category of list that developed in the last century for which no criteria are laid down, but instead they are at the whim of the compiler. In the UK the major and most popular lists in this type have been compiled for the Lake District. Perhaps this is not surprising since the Lake District is a compact area and very popular with tourists who flock to enjoy the scenery. It is a landscape that combines rugged mountains with lakes and manicured fields in the valleys and this landscape has drawn visitors from all over the world for the last couple of centuries. The more adventurous of these tourists have wished to explore the scenery in more intimate detail and perhaps this has been the catalyst for hill lists for this area alone.

As mentioned earlier, one of the first lists for the Lake District was published in 1937 by F Simpson for the 2,000ft hills. In 1955, however, a new phenomenon arrived on the bookshelves of local shops. It was entitled *A Pictorial Guide to the Lakeland Fells: Book One The Eastern Fells* and the author was Alfred Wainwright.

Wainwright's volume was the first of seven to be published between 1955 and 1966 covering all the Lake District; the last was The Western Fells. It should be stressed that these volumes did not comprise a list. Instead each is meticulously and uniquely laid out, with pen-and-ink illustrations, descriptions of summit views, maps and sketches of other hills to be seen from each summit, as well as illustrations of the scenery of the area. The volumes also describe, in detail, routes of ascent and natural features to be seen along the way. Another characteristic of the volumes is that all appear to be hand-written; a type face has not been used and thus the work has a unique presentation. It was probably a combination of this unique style combined with the detailed information in the Pictorial Guides that meant they soon became very popular. In the introduction to volume one Wainwright imparts to the reader his deep passion for the area; 'childhood's dreams', 'dear memories', 'another day of freedom on the hills', 'autumn colours', 'storm and tempest in high places'. Many of us might identify with some of those thoughts.

The choice of hills for the books was Wainwright's; there was no set criterion. All but one of the fells are 1,000ft or above; the exception was Castle Crag in Borrowdale which is only 951ft high. Many also feel that Wainwright was playing a prank on his readers when he included Mungrisdale Common in book 5 The Northern Fells. This feature is but a slight rise of a few metres on a long flat ridge that falls NW from Foule Crag on Blencathra.

In all 214 fells are presented in the set of books and these now form the list which many walkers in the Lake District aspire to climb.

Over the years since the publication of Wainwright's books changes have occurred to footpaths, right of access and topography and the growth in car travel has led to requests for parking information. This resulted in a revision of the volumes by Chris Jesty, and these are now available and a further edition is planned.

In 2002 the Wainwright Society was formed and now has a membership of about one thousand people. It promotes fellwalking through Wainwright's publications and contributes to issues affecting the landscape and quality of life, in upland areas of Britain and particularly the Lake District. Fellwalkers who climb all 214 Wainwrights may record their achievement with the Society. Many hundreds of people are known to have climbed the Wainwrights although there are probably many hundreds more who have not recorded their achievement. The Wainwrights are big business!

Following completion of his Pictorial Guides, Wainwright was urged to write more on fell walking in the Lake District. This resulted in *The Outlying Fells* which was first published in 1974 in the Westmorland Gazette, and later by Michael Joseph in 1992 and 1998. Once again the book was not intended to contain a list and there were no criteria set for the inclusion of hills in the book other than the fact that the hills lay on the extremities of Lakeland. The 116 hills described were chosen by Wainwright on the basis that he was now catering for older walkers who, because of their age or other impediments would be constrained to undertaking less demanding expeditions on lesser fells. *The Outlying Fells* may not be as popular as the Wainwrights, but for those who have completed that list and are looking for new areas to explore in Lakeland, then this list fulfils that objective.

Wainwright's books had encouraged many people to explore for themselves the Lake District and the sheer volume of interest created opportunities for others. Bill Birkett comes from a family of rock climbers, is an accomplished rock climber in his own right and also lives in the Lake District. It is therefore no surprise that in 1994 he wrote *Complete Lakeland Fells*. The book is a series of 129 circular walks which cover fell tops over 1,000ft within the National Park. No drop criterion is used and some tops are just changes in gradient on a ridge, despite appearing prominent from the valley below. But this misses the point; the book is a book of walks, not a list of hills. It is well set out and well-illustrated, hence its popularity. It is this popularity that has prompted some to undertake the challenge of doing all of these walks and thereby climb all the 541 tops described in the book. Consequently, the Birketts, as they are called, have been made into a list by others in much the same way as have the Wainwrights. Well over sixty people are known to have completed the list.

Finally, mention should be made of one other Lakeland list, namely the Synges. In 1997 Tim Synge created a list of hills lying within the Lake District National Park. His list comprises summits that are over 300 metres in height. Additionally, Castle Crag is included although this is below 300m. Since the author wished to include the Wainwrights within his list, and Castle Crag is a Wainwright, this would appear to be the justification for its inclusion. The list is divided into 'separate fells', that is hills with 30m or more of drop, and 'subsidiary tops' which are summits with less than 30m of drop, but the choice of the latter for inclusion in the list is subjective. Each fell is given a different symbol on the accompanying maps to denote its status (600m or over; separate fell; Wainwright). The symbols denote which of these attributes apply to the hill in question. There are 647 Synges comprising 244 separate fells and 403 subsidiary tops.

We have included the list in this chapter since it is a list that is a combination of criteria and also author's choice. Will this approach represent another opportunity for would-be authors of hill lists to exploit?

Southern Scotland

One of the curious features of various editions of the book of *Munro's Tables* has been the inclusion of Percy Donald's list of hills in the 'Scottish Lowlands', while hills in the rest of Scotland below 2,500ft were not included until 1997. Like Munro, Donald introduced two categories, hills and tops. He went further than Munro by defining rules for the distinction, but these rules were so complicated that few can remember them or even understand them, so it is easier to regard the Donalds as a personal list. Alan Dawson attempted to simplify matters by defining *New Donalds* as hills over 2,000ft with 30m drop, but this list has now been superseded by the Simms and also incorporated into the Tumps. David Purchase continued to honour Percy Donald's name by listing all the hills from 500m to 2,000ft high with 30m drop and calling them the Donald Deweys. By the end of 2017 seven people had climbed all 248 of these hills.

Central Scotland

Lists of hills have been compiled for the Ochils and the Pentlands, with suitably contrived acronyms. One of the advantages of the introduction of the all-encompassing Tumps has been that these acronyms and lists can now be laid to rest.

Whitehope Law, a Donald in the Moorfoot Hills (Derek Sime)

Wales

The substantial work of Myrddyn Phillips in listing and surveying the hills of Wales means that Wales probably has a higher density of listed hills than any region on earth other than the Lake District. His extensive historical and cultural enquiries have enabled him to identify names for a remarkable number of hills in his lists, which include Y Pedwarau (hills from 400m to 499m high with 30m drop) and hills over 500m high with 15m drop.

Above: Tryfan and Llyn Ogwen (Iain Robertson)

Below: On the Ridge to Crib y Ddysgl and Yr Wyddfa (David Batty)

Islands

Lists have been compiled of hills on Colonsay, the Isle of Man and other islands, but for hill baggers who like clear definitions, these have been superseded by the relevant subset of Tumps. Island bagging, and island hill bagging, has developed into a significant subculture in recent years, and so it was inevitable that a keen island aficionado would identify the need for a comprehensive list of islands. The resulting list was the Sibs (Significant Islands of Britain) and the compiler was Alan Holmes. Identifying islands is not quite as simple as it may seem, as there are tidal islands, river islands, bridged islands and the Channel Islands to consider, along with island area, island height and other factors. The lists of Sibs, main Sibs and Siblets are therefore still subject to revision. The author is confident that Ben Nevis will remain the highest island summit in Britain, but some consider that Mount Paget on South Georgia ought to come into consideration. Landing on many of the islands is extremely difficult, even with a boat, and so several of the current list of 566 Sibs have no recorded visits.

County Tops

The idea of visiting the highest point in each county has an obvious appeal for those who like travel and walking. However, in Britain there have been more revisions to counties and local authorities than there have to *Munro's Tables*. In both cases, 1974 was the fateful year. Some people choose to ignore the revisions and concentrate on visiting the highest point in each of the pre-1974 counties. Some of these historic area names live

TMS member John Green on the 'summit' of Lewesdon Hill, County Top of Dorset (John Green)

on as constituencies, cricket teams or country parks, such as Roxburghshire, Middlesex and Strathclyde. Some have been deleted and later reinstated, e.g. Rutland, while others have been introduced and then disbanded, e.g. Avon.

Apart from the regular meddling, there are other drawbacks to county tops as a baggable list. Several boundaries cross hills below the summit, so the highest point in some counties is an unidentifiable point on an unremarkable slope. For some unitary authorities and London boroughs, the highest point may be on a street corner. There is nothing wrong with collecting them but it has more in common with psychogeography than hill walking.

Despite these inherent deficiencies, some people do go to the trouble of visiting all the county tops, and books have been published on the subject. At least one renowned mountaineer, Alan Hinkes, is known to have bagged all the historic county tops, including the high point of Huntingdonshire. This point did not appear to have a name on any map, so one list compiler, who had never been to Huntingdonshire, decided that the name Boring Field would be appropriate. It is 81 metres high and has a drop estimated at one metre, although this has not been verified using satellite technology. The name has been adopted and is now in common use although, somewhat disappointingly, the appearance of a hedge and some sheds has made the summit area more interesting than originally thought. A comparison between the ascent of K2 and Boring Field would be of potential interest but has not yet been written. One record of the ascent of Boring Field referred to the 'pre-dawn stillness disturbed only by nearby sounds of country and western music ... was joined at both 'summits' by a friendly farm cat.' This extract from the expedition log illustrates the sense of exploration that encourages open-minded individuals to do things that most people would regard as ludicrous, which leads us back to hill surveying.

Surveyors have occasionally shown interest in county tops, perhaps out of a sense of duty rather than enthusiasm. G&J Surveys have investigated and confirmed the highest points in Wiltshire (Milk Hill), Nottinghamshire (Newtonwood Lane) and Vale of Glamorgan (Tair Onnen), while Alan Dawson has surveyed the highest point in the truncated version of Lancashire (Gragareth) and in various versions of Argyll (Bidean nam Bian and Ben Cruachan), amongst others.

The World

For many years Ireland was well behind Britain in hill listing evolution but it has made great progress in recent years, with a plethora of confusing categories to almost match anything on the other side of the Irish Sea. There is also an active GNSS surveying programme. Full details are included on the Hill Bagging website.

The extent of hill listing and peak bagging beyond the British Isles is variable but there are extensive lists on some impressive websites for those interested, e.g. Europeaklist, Peakbagger and Peakery. The most significant development in recent years has been the identification of the Ultras – summits with at least 1,500m of relative height. There are known to be over 1,520 of these, though the precise number is still being defined. There are thought to be 39 on Greenland and 39 on Antarctica, many of which are unclimbed. This is probably the ultimate hill bagging challenge on the planet. It is unlikely that anyone will ever be able to climb them all but the British are at the forefront, with Rob Woodall, Richard Mclellan and Denise Mclellan all past 200 and in the top four of the Ultra-bagging league table. The only other countries currently represented in the top 30 are Norway, the USA and Guatemala.

It is not known how much GNSS surveying has taken place beyond the British Isles, but GNSS surveys have been carried out on at least two significant summits: Everest and Denali. In both cases it was found that the original terrestrial surveys were remarkably accurate.

In recent years there has been extensive use of Lidar (aerial laser measurement) to identify summits and establish heights in the USA and elsewhere. It has limitations on vegetated or rocky summits but it has already proved to be useful in England and in Wales for identifying some col locations and unmapped man-made summits, as well as underground locations that are beyond the reach of satellite signals. Lidar data in Scotland is currently limited in scope and usefulness as it is expensive to generate and there is less demand.

A Swiss Ultra – Piz Bernina at sunrise, Oberengadin, Graubünden (Derek Sime)

Appendix A – List of Abbreviations

Furths	English, Welsh & Irish hills over 3,000ft high (the hills furth of Scotland)
GLONASS	Global Navigation Satellite System (Russian)
GNSS	Global Navigation Satellite System
GPS	Global Positioning System
HDOP	Horizontal Dilution of Precision
MBA	Mountain Bothies Association
MQI	Mountain Quality Indicator
MSL	Mean Sea Level
ODN	Ordnance Datum Newlyn
OS	Ordnance Survey
OSGB	Ordnance Survey Great Britain
OSGM	Ordnance Survey Geoid Model
RINEX	Receiver Independent Exchange
RTK	Real Time Kinematic
SD	Standard Deviation
SMC	Scottish Mountaineering Club
SMCJ	Scottish Mountaineering Club Journal
SMT	Scottish Mountaineering Trust
SQC	Statistical Quality Control
TMS	The Munro Society
VDOP	Vertical Dilution of Precision
WGS	World Geodetic System

Appendix B – List of Participants in the Heightings

TMS HELPERS
Alf Barnard
David Batty
Glen Breaden
Alan Brook
John Burdin
Irvine Butterfield
Anne Butler
Angus Campbell
Ian Collie
David Cran
Alan Dawson
John Green
Alan Haworth
Patrick Hetherington
Eleanore Hunter
Stewart Logan
Walter McArthur
Alistair Milner
Charles Murray
Iain Robertson
John Rogerson
John Ross
Susan Sharpe
Derek Sime
Findlay Swinton
Bill Taylor
Alex Thomson
Colin Walter
Fred Ward
Bill Wheeler
Peter Willimott

THE SURVEYORS
John Barnard
Liam Hill
Graham Jackson
Jim Melville
Evangelos Pentzas
Myrddyn Phillips

SMC
Rab Anderson
Andy Nisbet
Noel Williams

GUESTS
Barbara Barnard
Iain Brown
Bob Kyle
Beryl Milner
Chris Townsend

Appendix C – Chronological List of the Heightings

HILL	DATE
Beinn Dearg (1st attempt)	22nd April 2007
Foinaven	12th May 2007
Beinn Dearg	25th August 2007
Beinn Teallach	15th May 2009
Ben Vane	16th May 2009
Sgùrr a' Choire-bheithe	14th July 2009
Sgùrr nan Ceannaichean	15th July 2009
Geal-charn	16th April 2010
Beinn a' Chlèibh	30th July 2010
The Fara	31st July 2010
Beinn a' Chlaidheimh	4th July 2011
Beinn Dearg Mòr	6th July 2011
Ruadh Stac Mòr	8th July 2011
Leathad an Tobhain	15th June 2012
Beinn Bhreac	16th June 2012
Knight's Peak	11th September 2013
Bhàsteir Tooth	13th September 2013
Meall Gaineimh	27th May 2015
Ben Lawers (German TV)	28th July 2015
Carn na Caim	30th July 2015

Index

ff: following on from   fn: footnote   HTM: Hugh T Munro

photographic references in **_Bold Italic_** _(photographer and/or subject)_

The Munro Society

The Munro Society (TMS) was formed in 2002 and membership is open to anyone who has climbed all the Munros. When founded TMS was to be more than a club and social network, although these were important aspects. It was hoped that TMS would establish a 'voice' in matters pertaining to Scotland's mountain landscape. A membership comprising individuals who had climbed all the Munros was seen as a real strength in terms of credibility and substance. TMS differs from most other hill-walking clubs, not only in the entry qualification but also in having no geographical base, with 40% of members residing outside Scotland. Membership is growing and now exceeds 300. As with many clubs, there are fewer young people. It is a fact for TMS that most people are older by the time they compleat the Munros.

Although TMS lacks a geographical base the thrice-yearly weekend meets are well attended. Three Newsletters are published each year and a Journal or similar publication every two years. The AGM in April is followed by lunch and talks from members and invited speakers. The Annual Dinner in October is preceded by a lecture and followed by a mountain photography competition and an after-dinner talk. TMS hosts the Irvine Butterfield memorial lecture, in memory of a founding member and its first President, at the annual Dundee Mountain Film Festival held in November.

An ethos of the Society is that future generations should have access to the thinking and activities of those who preceded them on the mountains. An archive has been established, concentrating on matters germane to Munros and Munroists, based at the AK Bell Library in Perth. It contains a thorough record of TMS activities, individual records, diaries and logs and a series of interviews with early Munroists, stored on DVD.

The TMS Constitution states that the Society should be 'an informed and authoritative body of opinion and influence on the protection of and access to the Munros and their mountain landscape and Scotland's mountains in general'. Members have a huge collective understanding of the changes to the hill environment over the last few decades. The accelerated loss of and impact on wild land in recent times, particularly from industrial scale wind farms, poorly constructed run-of-river hydro schemes and unregulated tracks, has been very obvious. TMS endorses the position of Mountaineering Scotland, which 'supports the Scottish Government's aim of developing clean, renewable energy sources but opposes developments that threaten the wild landscape of Scottish mountains'.

An early initiative was the introduction of Mountain Quality Indicators of Environment and Experience (MQIs) which has evolved into Mountain Reports (MRs): **www.tmsmountainreports.net**. They have been completed by more than 30 members, contributing more than 2,000 reports to date. They provide a solid body of information across a range of subject matter pertinent to Scotland's mountain landscape, including access, flora, fauna, human impact, erosion and members' general observations and responses. Before this resource was established, although members had many significant observations about Scotland's mountain landscape, these were subjective, reliant on memory, difficult to quantify and not recorded.

www.themunrosociety.com